"Peter has a unique way with words: he makes you appreciate
anew the preciousness of the present moment."
David Bradford, Cycling Weekly

Andy Jordan, Founder/Chief Creative Officer of Needle
Space Labs and maker of a video described by the Alzheimer's
Society as one of the best of its kind, calls Peter's
story 'powerful and inspirational.'

SLOW
PUNCTURE

PETER BERRY & DEB BUNT

The Book Guild Ltd

First published in Great Britain in 2020 by
The Book Guild Ltd
9 Priory Business Park
Wistow Road, Kibworth
Leicestershire, LE8 0RX
Freephone: 0800 999 2982
www.bookguild.co.uk
Email: info@bookguild.co.uk
Twitter: @bookguild

Typeset in 11pt Minion Pro

Printed and bound in the UK by TJ International, Padstow, Cornwall

ISBN 978 1913208 936

British Library Cataloguing in Publication Data.
A catalogue record for this book is available from the British Library.

For my father, Jimmy Berry (Elderberry) 1926–2019, whose immortal words, "I have a bad memory you know, Peter, but I never forget it if I think of it," have stayed with me always.

Acknowledgements

Thanks must go to Sue for her effective coaching session on the first day of the 2019-20 football season (if only the Arsenal manager would listen to her), Howard for his time and constructive appraisal, Martin for his patience, love and his wonderful spreadsheets, Peter's Facebook readers for their encouragement, Charmian for the chance meeting and her photography and, of course, Peter and Teresa for letting me into their lives and for being such great friends.

FOREWORD

BY WENDY MITCHELL
BEST-SELLING AUTHOR OF
SOMEBODY I USED TO KNOW

When you've met one person with dementia, you've simply met one person with dementia. We all have our own unique stories to tell, none less important than another. I've met Peter and Teresa on a few of our 'gatherings' and always been comforted by their closeness, their 'teamwork', against this bummer of a diagnosis.

Peter's book is a story of the depths to which dementia can plummet your mind, as well as the strength found to overcome the challenges. His mirror image experience of his father is tragic, whereas his newfound love of a simple penny farthing and the joy it can bring, is uplifting.

As a couple their lives run in parallel and highlight the changing relationships that evolve. The one poignant sentence which says this with ease:

"Teresa 'suffers' from the effects of dementia, whereas Peter 'lives' with dementia."

PROLOGUE

"My world turns outside my head now, sometimes a distant planet in the solar system of my life. Thoughts become shooting stars that fly past me but don't actually stop, colourful as they pass, but quickly fading into the horizon. It's like I'm a small planet in a big solar system with many other bigger planets surrounding me and I'm getting smaller."

These are Peter Berry's words when we discuss writing a book. Diagnosed with early onset dementia at the age of fifty and living with this brutal, progressive condition means Peter now struggles to put pen to paper, or finger to keyboard. I have noted how his frustration has become more palpable with each month that passes. There is so much he wants to say, so many ideas are bubbling around in his mind that it seems to me, as I listen to him, that they are in danger of overboiling. There is so much he wants to share with others and so much about himself he wishes to preserve for himself and his family. And yet he is stuck in a quagmire of frustration; with the passing of each week, each month and each year, a little more of Peter's world is sucked further into the mire where it remains, at first gurgling gently just on the surface, and then decaying, before being lost forever. He cannot write about his life or tell a story of a remarkable year without help. And, most tragically, he will never read the story of his life which he has asked me to tell.

However, as with many things in Peter's world, a problem is merely the prelude to a solution, and thus an idea is born. We agree that I will write his book for him, using his words but breathing life into them, so they become tangible for others to see.

It is, perhaps, a cruel paradox that Peter's dementia, which is chipping away at his world and shrinking it, has created a whole new world for me. The dementia, which has sealed off some of the doors in his memory, has become the key which has unlocked a delightful part of the country for me and widened my horizons, and for that I will be forever grateful. As much as the dementia has stripped Peter bare in so many ways, it seems to feed me, to enrich me and, in a curious twist of events, his dementia has become empowering for me. The positive side to Peter's dementia has been that it has given him the opportunity to share the world that he loves so much with someone who is eager to be a part of it. And, most importantly, by doing so, it has given him back some element of who he was: a man at the hub of things, a man who knew and could make decisions.

When we go cycling, it is Peter who chooses our cycle routes and Peter who navigates our journeys. It is Peter who gives the all-clear at junctions, Peter who will deal with any mechanical issues, and it is Peter who has the expertise and wherewithal to repair any puncture. When I am out with Peter, I feel safe and contained, and I think he knows that and thrives on it.

My first year in Suffolk has been a remarkable journey for me, but it is a journey which has only been possible because I am riding it with Peter and watching as he refuses to be beaten down by his condition. But, of course, despite his defiance and fist-waving in the face of his dementia monster, there is not going to be a magical ending to this story, no unexpected twists or turns. There simply cannot be. The tragic truth is that dementia will be the winner and although Peter, after a good day, might say, "Peter Berry 1, Alzheimer's 0," eventually the match is going to end and dementia will be the savage victor, even if Peter manages to drag it into extra time and a penalty shoot-out.

But I am not interested in endings, nor do I have any desire to think about them. I am interested in charting my new beginnings and the incredible things a man with dementia has done over the four seasons I have known him. I am sure he will continue to do more amazing things, but I want to capture my first year in Suffolk via Peter. Peter's energy and positivity makes me humble but also puts me in awe of him, although he is always embarrassed to hear me say it.

Above all, I want to write this book because Peter once said to me, "I'm afraid I'm going to forget who I am and the things that I can do." When I think about all the things Peter has given to me, I can't think of anything better to give back to Peter than to help preserve his identity and to record his thoughts, actions and poetry by writing them down before they disintegrate into a powdery dust and are lost forever.

Peter is a man who expresses his emotions and feelings with considerable poetical panache. He says to me, "Sometimes it's like I'm standing in a forest in the fog and I'm trying to shine a flashlight to see what's out there, but the light bounces back to me and blinds me."

This forest image is uncannily apposite: Peter owned and ran the family timber business, J.W. Berry's, before he was forced to sell up. There cannot be many woods or trees in Suffolk which the Berry bunch have not worked in.

But now he does not work. Now he does not drive. Always fiercely independent and determined, always at the hub of family life, he has had to allow some of his autonomy to be removed from him.

"Dementia has taken so much from me," he says. "My income, my self-esteem, my future." He pauses. "But here's a thing: I have taken so much from dementia. I live every day; I enjoy every day. I might forget it moments later, but I have learned to live in the moment and that's a wonderful, precious thing to do. How lucky am I? They say you only live once, but that's rubbish: you only die once. You live every day. And that's what I fully intend to do."

Peter's smile lights up the room, shining a shaft of light across it and creating a clear swathe through the fogginess to reveal his world. For that fleeting moment, I see inside his world just a little bit more.

This is a world Peter wants to be shared so that others, touched by dementia in some way, can take heart. He wants them to know that a diagnosis of dementia does not mean the end of the journey, but the beginning of a new one, and above all he wants to get the message out there that, "Life isn't over with dementia, it's just a little different."

CHAPTER
ONE
PETER'S STORY

(i)

Here's a thing: years ago, my father said to me, "Peter, you aren't working for me until you've got yourself a pension." Well, I was fifteen and a half. I was more interested in chasing girls and buying bikes than having a pension. Why would a red-blooded youngster like me, living in rural Suffolk, want to think about pensions and the future? But I sorted a pension out and, do you know what, thank God I did, especially as nowadays I'm more interested in buying bikes than chasing girls. I suppose you could say I was lucky, which is an odd thing to say when you're living with a terminal condition but, you know, sometimes it feels like I am lucky.

These are some of the reasons: I get to live every day as if it were a new day; people tell me their news or the things we are going to do and, because my short-term memory is so terribly poor, I quickly forget and then I relive the moment. It's like unwrapping the same present every time without realising that it's a gift you've already received. Last year, my friend, Deb, gave me a birthday card which I laughed at so much that she asked to take it back and then she gave it to me the next day and, apparently, I laughed again. Some might say that was a bit unkind, but not me. I think that's a funny story. Mind you, I don't remember that, I have to take her word for it that it happened. And let's face it, if you don't laugh at tragedy, you're going to cry.

But how cool is that to get to enjoy the same moment more than once! So, you see, these days I live in my own dementia bubble where every day brings a new surprise. It's not many folks who get to say that.

I get to see the colours of Suffolk and to hear the birds singing or I get to see a newly planted tree or even an old tree which Father planted, and this gives me pause for thought and reflection. Because my time is so precious, I now take the time to enjoy the things around me for what they are and to live in the moment, rather than to worry about the next moment. When you constantly look for the next part of your life, you miss the present moments of your life. We spend so much time worrying about what might happen, that we forget to enjoy what is happening.

But mainly I am lucky just because I am still alive.

Perhaps, I'm not so lucky in that I'm living with a terminal condition with my early onset dementia, but no one ever said that life was perfect.

Let me backtrack a bit. That's the thing about this dementia: it's a rum thing, a strange old journey and it can take you to all sorts of places in all sorts of unexpected directions, but that's absolutely fine because, for me, it's about the journey, not the destination. Let's face it, I know what the destination is going to be. I just don't know the exact route or how long it's going to take me to reach it. But I do know that I don't want to reach it. So, I do a few twists and turns to stretch the journey out a little bit longer because the alternative, the arrival at my destination, is not a place I want to get to.

I want to tell you a little about my father, Jimmy Berry, because he has always been a really important part of my life and, even though he died a few months ago (which I keep forgetting, which makes me feel a bit of an idiot, although I believe Father would have seen the funny side), he will remain one of the most influential people I have ever met.

Father left school without much of an education, but he taught himself to read and write. He worked like a dog from morning till night, learning everything he could about timber and trees and the countryside, and then, in 1947, he started his timber business from nothing and he built it up until it was renowned throughout Suffolk.

Father used to say, "You can be driven and be uneducated or you can be driven and educated, but if you're not driven, you aren't going to be going anywhere in life."

And, as with most things, he was right. Semi-literate he might have been, but he was canny and motivated, and his business grew as steady as an oak tree. He and Mother had five sons and we lived a great life in a small market town called Framlingham in Suffolk. My playground was the mere around Framlingham Castle or the woods adjoining the town. We had freedom and made our own entertainment. But the thing I enjoyed the most was riding my bike or fixing my bike or reading about bikes. That was my childhood. I had a little shed in our back garden where I stored bike components. I had a sign on the door, 'Peter's Bike Shed', and I spent a lot of my teenage years just fixing mine or others' bikes and learning about how they worked.

I left school, followed Father's advice and got myself a pension, and I went to work for him when I was fifteen and a half. I'd always had a special relationship with Father; I was happy to work with him and going to work became a pleasure, not a chore. I learned so much from him, but he was very understated about how he taught me. He never bossed me about or told me I had to do it his way. I listened to him and I learned how to work with trees and how to treat people well: I was fortunate to have a father who taught me so much.

Twenty years ago, Father was diagnosed with Alzheimer's. Before he received his diagnosis, I had realised that his memory was doing strange things and the business was teetering on the edge of going under. But he still retained his ability to talk and to look at life in his own unique way. I think he knew what was happening to him, but he never really let on except for once, when we were sitting in the office, surrounded by paperwork, trying to restore order to the mess. He was looking confused and holding pieces of paper in his hands helplessly, without really knowing what to do with them, but desperate to do *something* with them. He looked at me and his eyes were sad, as though he knew he was going to be defeated.

"Peter, my boy," he said, "It could happen to a bishop."

There was a certain chilling accuracy about his prediction which I did not realise at that time.

As his memory deteriorated, I took over the running of the business and got it back in the black, and then things just improved until it became a thriving enterprise again. I made sure I included Father in as much of the business as I could because, even then, I knew that putting someone on the scrap heap was not the decent thing to do. Of course, then, when I was powerful and in charge of my own life, I had no idea that when I looked at Father, I was staring into the face of my own future.

The business started to do really well again and there wasn't a tree or a wood in Suffolk that hadn't had the Berry touch to it. Now, when I cycle around the countryside, I can still spot the woods where we felled trees, or where a particularly stubborn tree remains or even where Father told me that, as a youngster just starting out in life, he fell asleep under a tree because he was too tired to cycle the fifteen miles home on his old rickety bike after a twelve-hour day at work.

I worked really hard for twenty years and employed twelve men directly. I sub-contracted up to seventeen additional men and we had five trucks. Just like Father before me, I was always fair and treated people well. I valued other people's knowledge and experiences and always took care to listen to what my men said to me. I increased our turnover and it just felt as if life was as good as it could ever be.

I was a methodical and tidy worker, and very good at keeping the accounts and the list of orders. Everything was written down in big notebooks, which I still have, although I have no idea why I have kept over twenty notebooks with invoices and orders in them. I suppose it's a way of hanging on to my old life. My office was immaculate; everything had a place, and there was a place for everything.

People would come into the office and we'd discuss sizes of timber and types of wood. Then, perhaps weeks later, they'd come back and I'd recognise them and remember their order and the discussions we'd had. That used to amaze people that I could remember so much and so well. But that level of memory and attention to detail defined who I was and it was very important to me.

They were the good days – the sunny days, I suppose. My wife, Teresa, and I enjoyed our lives and then, when our daughter, Kate, was born, it seemed that we were truly blessed. We had enough money to live well, to take great holidays, to have new cars whenever we fancied. We didn't know that this would come to an end.

Gradually, without being aware of it at first, things just got a little cloudy and overcast, and I felt the beginnings of a cold chill across my neck. I'd be driving the truck around the countryside over routes that I knew so well, but I'd find myself muddled and not knowing where I was. Simple tasks, practical tasks, that had been second nature to me, started to confuse me.

Then I realised that I was losing bits of information but still refused to put a name to the cloud which was hanging over me. Well, we men can be a bit stubborn and often can refuse to see what might be staring at us directly in the face.

I'm just tired, I'd tell myself. *I have much too much to do.*

I started to order expensive equipment we didn't really need and the debts piled up. I refused to see it, though, and certainly refused to share it with Teresa. I was struggling but thought I was strong enough to get through it.

To try to regain control of the increasing chaos around me, I began to develop strategies to help me remember. One of those strategies was to jot things down on those yellow post-it notes and plaster them across the office. There must have been hundreds of them, all over the walls, covered in tiny handwriting. I reckon I must have kept the post-it note company in business!

Well, one day Teresa came into the office and saw how the walls were covered with these post-it notes, all with a barely legible scrawl across them. She gave me one of those looks that only wives can do.

When we talked about what the problem might be, we talked about brain tumours and became immersed in all the 'what-if' scenarios. We never really thought it would be dementia. Not at my age.

We spent several terrible days trying to summon up the courage to see the doctor and, when we did, he sent us off to a consultant.

Whilst we were waiting for our appointment, Teresa started to discover the full extent of how reckless my borrowing and spending had become. Apparently, I had borrowed large sums of money from friends and forgotten to pay them back. Teresa felt humiliated as she uncovered the true facts. She said people assumed I had been trying to dupe them or swindle them. Our village was very small and it was difficult not to bump into people we knew. I had no idea what I had done and I didn't realise how alienated she felt from the people who used to be our friends.

The day came for our visit to the consultant. I had a brain scan and then a series of tests.

What I don't really remember is this bit, the tests, so I have to assume my wife is telling the truth – as if she would lie to me! According to Teresa we were sitting in the consultant's office. The consultant asked me to write down as many words beginning with the letter 'p' as I could. Apparently, I sat there like a child in an exam they hadn't revised for; it was obvious I was going to fail.

Teresa said she tried to give me the answers by the power of her thoughts, but it didn't work, which is curious because when she does this at home – for example, when she's staring at me to get me to make a cup of tea or put the dishes away – I always pick up her thought waves, which can be very forceful, shall we say! But I just sat there and stared at the bit of paper. I couldn't think of one word which began with a letter 'p', which is ironic, really, when you think about my name.

I think we were both waiting to be told that I had a brain tumour. We sat there just waiting. And then we were shocked. The consultant told us there was nothing wrong with me and he sent us away. We were bewildered but assumed that everything would be all right (how naïve were we?).

A few weeks later, we received a call from someone else who had seen my brain scan and was alarmed by what she had seen. We went to see her and, just like that, she told us that I had early onset dementia. It was a brutal way to break the news but, you know, it was a curious thing because at first, after the diagnosis, I almost felt relieved.

I believed I even said to Teresa, "So it's not serious. It's not a brain tumour... We'll be fine."

But then, when we got home, we used our old friend Google to do our own research, and the extent of my condition started to become painfully clear.

This news was going to shatter our world forever. We knew that we would never be the same again. After another meeting with the medical people, we were told that my type of Alzheimer's would mean that my life expectancy would be maybe, eight or nine years.

We had been given just one leaflet and told to come back in a year's time. That's all we were given, that one leaflet. When you get a cancer diagnosis, you leave with several leaflets, with information about help groups, next appointments and dates for treatment. You have a sense of the pathway you will be travelling along. You don't get anything like that when you get a diagnosis of dementia. You're on your own. And we felt very much on our own, we really did.

Even a phone call from someone directly after the diagnosis would have helped. A simple, "Do you want me to pop round for a chat? Do you have any questions?", would have been welcomed. Then it would have been up to us to say yes or not. But there was nothing. It felt as if we had been cast adrift.

The thing is you don't go to a doctor on a Monday and then come out with dementia. You've had dementia for some time, and I reckoned I had had it for a good few years. All the doctor does is to confirm it or send you somewhere else to confirm it. You're still the same person as you were when you went to see him. But in that moment, I didn't feel like the same person at all. I wasn't Peter Berry, successful businessman, anymore. I wasn't even Peter Berry, normal bloke. I was now Peter Berry, living with Alzheimer's, or Peter Berry, the man that people would feel sorry for or take pity on or avoid in the street because they were too embarrassed to talk to him.

One of the things I often say (and apparently, I have a tendency to repeat myself because I can be forgetful… strange, that!) was that dementia was not just a diagnosis for the individual but a diagnosis for the whole family. Dementia was going to touch Kate and Teresa, although in different ways to how it affected me. My daughter was going to have to watch her powerful old dad become less able and less powerful (and probably never get to be that old) and she'd have to learn to live her life without me. If she ever had children, they would never know their granddad, except through photos or stories. And as for Teresa – well, she was going to go from a wife to a carer to a widow. That's not a journey that anyone should have to go through and certainly not one that she signed up for when we got married all those years ago.

We tried to find our own support. Teresa contacted the Citizens Advice Bureau. They put her in touch with Age Concern who put her in touch with Citizens Advice again. We went around in circles like that for a while. We ended up going to a meeting of carers for those living with Alzheimer's, but the room was full of old people, much older than me. Some of them were incontinent, others were dribbling or just staring vacantly ahead. You could see they'd 'gone' just by looking into their eyes. They had lost their soul somewhere in the murky depths of the dementia pond. It just was depressing and not at all relevant to me. I didn't want to watch people in their eighties sit in chairs, being cared for by relatives, without a clue about what was going on. I didn't want to see people further down the dementia journey and look at them knowing that was going to be me in a few years' time. How was that going to help me? I was young; I was only fifty years old.

A year or two down the line, we found a meeting about support groups which we hoped would be useful, and we all sat around a table. There was an agenda and minutes. I looked around the room; other people seemed so much more able than I to follow. I would be sitting there with absolutely no idea about what was going on and unable to keep up, watching other people – also with dementia – busily writing notes or referring back to things that had been said at previous meetings and I had no recollection about anything that had been said. It made me feel like a fool and I hated it. Other people, too, seemed so much more self-absorbed with their own failings and ailments than I was. I sat and watched people who were meant to be like me, with the same condition as I had, but I felt totally remote from them. Other people seemed to be defined by their dementia, obsessed by their ailments, fascinated by their deteriorating bodies, and it made me fearful for what I might become.

You know, I think that dementia is a drizzle that becomes a puddle and then a pool, and we look at our reflection in that pool when we look at those who are further along their dementia journey. I did not want to look at the reflection and I did not want to be out in that drizzle, catching a chill which was going to end up killing me. These people and their Alzheimer's were nothing to me. I had so many questions, but no one seemed to be able to help. I must say here, though, that since my awful experiences in seeking support, things have changed in Suffolk; there are more groups starting up now and this is a very good thing.

But then, back in those early bleak days, after attending meetings like this where Teresa and I felt more alone than ever, we decided that we would deal with our diagnosis on our own. Our household became a sad, lonely place, but the one thing we did agree on was that we weren't going to share our news with anyone outside the immediate family. Dementia had become our guilty secret, clutched close to our chests, burrowing its way into our lives until it formed a wedge between Teresa and me. The truth was I ashamed and embarrassed to have dementia. I felt like a fool and perhaps I believed in all of those old stereotypes which we see on the television, the sort of images where people with dementia are old and incapable. But by not telling people, we became more isolated and everything just got so much worse. I firmly believe now that keeping the news private was the worst thing we could have done and I urge anyone else who has received this bombshell not to keep it a secret but to seek support. It doesn't have to be from a recognised group, as often the support is all around you. You just have to seek it out. If you keep it secret, it will eat away at you and win the battle much more quickly – you have to fight back, you have to stand up and show it that you are not so easily cowed.

But at this point of the diagnosis and the journey ahead, we had made the decision to withdraw from much of our social life in the community. We live in a tiny village in Suffolk called Friston. Our village is a small community where most people know everyone else. There is a village hall, a pub and a church. Oh, and we also have two streetlights, unlike neighbouring Sternfield which has only one, and that sets Friston on a higher level. We sometimes look down on the folk from Sternfield and wonder how they cope! In Friston, there is also a playing field where I had planted a tree for Kate's second birthday. We called it 'Kate's tree', and it was my legacy for Kate. I've watched that tree grow from a sapling to the wonderful tree it is now, and I love the fact that Kate and the tree have grown up together. I often go and look at that tree, and it brings back some moving emotions for me. Nowadays, you see, I tend to remember by emotions and feelings rather than with memories.

In the meantime, Teresa tried to mop up the mess that the business had become and to pay off the debts. Clearing up the devastating trail of dementia destruction was just the beginning of our new journey and we found this tough enough. Keeping it a secret from most other people almost destroyed us.

One of the things which emerged from all of this financial mess and something which I felt passionately needs to be changed was the response of my bank.

I had paid in to the insurance policy for over twenty years in case I became terminally ill and couldn't work and therefore couldn't pay the mortgage. I never missed a payment. On receiving the dementia diagnosis, I contacted the bank to see how quickly payments could be made to me from the policy. I was told that dementia was not listed as a terminal condition and therefore the payments I had been making for years were effectively worthless. The other side to that was that I couldn't remortgage the house or take out a loan because the bank did not think I would be in a position to pay anything back because… wait for it… I had a terminal illness. You couldn't make it up.

I really did not want Teresa to lose the house and for her and Kate to be homeless and penniless. The thought appalled me. Whilst I was still able, I worked like a dog, and every penny I earned went into paying off the mortgage. And when it became obvious to me that I couldn't really run the business in any meaningful way – even with help – I stepped down. I was left literally sweeping the yard – imagine it – running a broom about the yard of the business that my father had started, a business that I had nurtured and that had flourished under my guidance. I was not going to allow myself to be humiliated like this. I thought, *no, I can't and I won't do this.* So, I put the broom down and stepped away from all aspects of the business.

But I still get very angry when I think about this and how unfair the system was, and I want people to know that this was yet another inequity dementia dealt to us. Had I had cancer or any other terminal condition, my policy would have stood and I would not have gone through such humiliation and pain.

As another aside, whilst I am on a rant, I also have to pay for my medication, unlike those living with cancer, for whom their medication is free. It's not as if my tablets are something I can choose to live without. My tablets turbocharge me, they fire constant messages to my brain and spark it into life. They do not treat the problem of dementia and they certainly don't cure it; they just manage the symptoms. I will never be cured of my dementia and I will probably die of it, rather than with it. So, the tablets are essential for me. At the moment, I am on the strongest dose of medication and so when the tablets begin to fail (which they inevitably will do), I too will fail. I have noticed that I am now forgetting to take my tablets as well but, like with all things, methods and strategies can be put into place to help me remember. On the days when Teresa leaves early for work, Deb will text me to remind me to take them. Yes, of course this feels like I am a child, but without my tablets, I will grind to a halt and so I bite back the rising aggravation of being a five-year-old for the pay-off of remaining alive and functioning. My tablets are an integral part of my life. And yet... and yet... I still have to pay for them. I wish someone high up in authority would just tell me why. If I had had some responsibility for my condition, say, by smoking and then contracting lung cancer, or eating too much cheese and then having poor cholesterol, or drinking too heavily and then having liver failure, I would accept the consequences, but I had done nothing in my life to encourage the dementia to take root in my brain and yet it felt as if I was being blamed somehow by being made to pay for it just in order to continue to live.

Accessing benefits after diagnosis was another thing which angered us all: after a huge amount of paperwork and talking on the phone and running through our story repeatedly – something which, let's be honest, no one with this sort of diagnosis wants to do – Teresa managed to get our council tax reduced by £25 a month. We also get a personal living allowance. But we get nothing else. And we have just been told that if Teresa is granted a carer's allowance, some of the discount from the council tax reduction will be taken away. They give with one hand; they take back with the other. After years of paying into the system, we were left empty-handed. That was just not right.

So that's the end of my rant!

Like I said, the diagnosis of dementia was one for the whole family and I watched it tear into our family's relationships. Kate found it tough to cope and wouldn't talk about it, and Teresa and I – well, our relationship suffered too. In almost a blink of an eye or a decaying bit from a brain cell, we had gone from a couple who talked and joked and went out to socialise, to a couple who lived in an eerie, uneasy silence, weighed down by the fear that our nasty little secret would escape and that we would pitied by others or be the object of fun or, worse still, become targets to ruthless scammers who preyed on the vulnerable. And as much as I hated the word 'vulnerable', there was no getting away from it. That's what I was destined to become.

(ii)

As we get older, many people worry about getting dementia. And of course, you might have one of those 'tip of the tongue' moments when you grapple around for the word but just can't quite bring it to your mind. Or you might experience that annoying thing when you can't think where you put the car keys and you say, "Oh, I'm losing my mind." And you will probably say it as a joke, not for a moment thinking that one day you might actually be diagnosed with the condition. You might tell other people about this funny thing that happened to you about losing the car keys, but they were in your pocket all the time and they'd say, "Oh yes, that happens to me... obviously we are all going senile." And you'd all laugh and then you'd think no more of it. Because, let's face it, senility is hugely amusing, isn't it?

But let me tell you: that is not dementia, that's just plain forgetfulness and we all suffer from that in this frenetic world. Dementia means that eventually you will never find the right word; dementia means you have the car keys in your hand, but you can't think for the life of you what to do with them. Dementia means walking into your house and not knowing if the bathroom is upstairs or downstairs. Dementia means not knowing if you've eaten breakfast or even if you're hungry. Dementia means that one day, if something else doesn't kill you first, you will be left staring vacantly into space not knowing who you are. Dementia means that bit by bit, piece by piece, your body will just stop functioning. And, of course, dementia means living in a state of constant, gut-wrenching fear. Sometimes when I wake up in the morning (on the nights I am lucky enough to sleep, that is), I do a sort of body inventory where I run through each part of my body, seeing which ability in the night has been removed. Once another ability has been taken away, you know you will never get it back. I feel like I am waiting for the next part of my former life to be carved away from me until there really is nothing left other than the shell. You have to be a strong person to live with this every day.

Here's a thing: think for a moment about your own brain. It's there in your head, doing all the things it should be doing: it helps you walk and talk and breathe. It sends messages to your eyes so you can share in everything the world offers, both good and bad. It tells you when something smells good or bad; it tells you when you're hungry and thirsty. It reminds you of fun things to come or sad things that have gone. Basically, it tells you how to function as a human being. You probably barely give it a second thought. Now think about my brain. My brain is gradually shrinking into my head until, one day, it won't be there at all. My head will be the same size as it is now, but there will be nothing of any value left inside. On a scan, all you would see would be a mass of black where the brain cells had died. Of course, I would still be there, but that's not much use if my brain had gone. I wonder how you would feel if you were living with this. I'm hoping you're going to say absolutely petrified because that's pretty much how I feel every day. I am absolutely terrified by the future.

And I wonder what you would find worse: knowing what's coming or the actual disease itself when it finally arrives in its appalling entirety? For me, it's like watching something lurking in the distance, gradually edging towards you, and you know you are going to get flattened by it and that you can't dodge it or hide, but what you don't know is which bit of your body is going to be flattened first and so you can't brace yourself for the blow.

So, with this diagnosis and with the knowledge of what was going to come, it was fair to say that this was a dark time. A very dark time. And we couldn't see a way out. As if in preparation for my shrinking world, the walls of the house seemed to close in on us and I found it hard to breathe and think. I became more depressed and my sense of worth took a battering. I felt hopeless, useless and worthless. From the hub of family life, from the man who could solve all problems, I had become an empty shell. I could see the effect it had on Teresa, too. She became withdrawn. At first, she didn't eat more than one small meal a day. When I tried to get her to eat, she said, "I can't. I'm so full of everything that's going on. I think I'd be sick if I ate. I'm full of pain. There's no room inside me for anything else."

Teresa said she felt as if she was walking with a cloud just over her head, ready to burst at any time. She never could get away from the cloud. This is what I meant by dementia wasn't just my diagnosis but a diagnosis for the whole family. Teresa carried the diagnosis around with her all day, every day, and became drawn and pale. And then, after a while, she began to eat, recklessly and compulsively, and she put on weight. She didn't want to talk about it or think about our future. I suppose I should say her future, because I wasn't really convinced I had much of a future. And we didn't even talk about the past anymore. We were left very much with the lurking presence of my diagnosis.

From the silence of the early days immediately after the diagnosis, things eventually changed again and we bickered a lot. It was as if the house couldn't catch its breath without choking on the stench of dementia and arguing was the only way to pierce a hole in the cloud which hung over us. We were all affected, Teresa, Kate and me.

What, I thought, was the point to me being alive? I thought my family would be better off without me. I had nothing to offer them except a future full of distress and dark times. I was destined to fall into a dank dungeon, from which there would be no escape, but from which I would need constant care. People would be looking down at me with pity, pointing at me as if I couldn't see them, talking about me, making decisions for me whilst I writhed helplessly in the pit below. I did not want that. I was in a place where no human being should ever have to go to and could only see one way out.

One September morning, I drove the truck down to Blaxhall where the railway line crosses the road. I parked up carefully and then I stood by the track, checking my watch. I knew what time the train was due and I also knew that this had to be a carefully timed suicide attempt as there was only one train an hour on this line and I really didn't fancy waiting another hour of my life before being flattened by a train. I just wanted it over and done with. I reckoned it must be much easier in London to chuck yourself under a train, but here in Suffolk you had to plan your suicide attempt like a military operation. I stood there for a while, and then when the train was scheduled to come, I stood, straddling the track, eyes closed, bracing myself for the moment of impact, thinking about all the things I had achieved and the people I was going to let down, and I wondered if they'd be angry or a little relieved that I wasn't going to be a burden on them. I wondered how much it would hurt and if my death would be quick and painless. But the train did not come and, to be honest, I felt like a bit of a fool, just standing there waiting. After twenty minutes of waiting, I abandoned this particular suicide attempt and wandered away. I half thought about writing a letter of complaint to the manager of Greater Anglia: "Dear sir, your inefficiency has thwarted my suicide attempt. Have some consideration for your customers and please ensure this does not happen again." (Later that evening, whilst watching the local news, I found out that they'd cancelled the train – points failure at Lowestoft. I mean, really!)

With this suicide attempt derailed, as it were, I popped home for my usual healthy lunch (which, looking back, is slightly weird – surely I should have indulged in the biggest, fattest burger and chips and cake I could have found!) and never said a word to Teresa about what I had been planning to do. Then, after lunch, I took myself down to the timber yard; I looked around that yard and remembered how Father had built it up and then lost it, and how I rebuilt it for him and now it had gone under again. I remembered Father saying, "It could happen to a bishop," and not really knowing what he meant. Now I understood exactly what he meant and wondered if he had known something even then about the way my life was going to be.

I admired Father so much and I was so like him in many ways. Once, years ago, when I was opening a packet of sugar at my uncle's house and opening it methodically and neatly as I always did, my uncle looked at me and said, "Your father will never be dead whilst you're alive, boy," but I didn't want to be like him and live with this Alzheimer's and slowly decline. What was the use of that?

The train might have been cancelled but I was still in charge of my destiny. I was always a very practical man, able to turn my hands to most tasks. I made a good, sturdy noose out of some rope, climbed up on the tractor and I put the noose around my neck. The rope scratched at my skin. It was heavy on my neck and I could feel it pull at my Adam's apple. I was at a dark place where no human being ought to be. I was on the edge of the abyss looking down. It certainly looked inviting down there. Then I put one leg out and balanced on the other leg. All I had to do was to step off. It was odd. I thought this would be the point when my heart would be pounding and I would be full of fear. But I was very calm. It was as if my body was telling me to step off. *Do it, Berry, do it!* I stood there, balanced on the edge, just thinking. I remember thinking that I'd just bought some expensive new glasses and that was going to be a bit of a waste of money. Ever the businessman, I suppose I was calculating the cost of the glasses and offsetting it against the worthlessness of my life.

And then there was a moment, nothing to do with my new glasses. It was like a light came on and it seemed to shine across my path showing me the next part of my life as, suddenly, I felt I had a clear mission. Who had been there for me, I thought? No one. What help had Teresa and I received? None. That just wasn't right. I didn't want anyone else to go through what I was going through. For the time that I had left – and I had no idea how much time that was going to be – I was going to be the person there for others; I was going to be the person that I wished had been there for me when I got my diagnosis. I was going to be the ordinary bloke in the street who would make sure that no one went through the dark hell of what I had to go through. After all, what I had planned to do was a long-term solution to a short-term problem. I've always been one to problem-solve. So, I got down and took the noose off my neck and I said out loud, "It's Peter Berry 1, Alzheimer's 0."

(iii)

THE DEMENTIA MONSTER GETS AN IDENTITY

And here was the extraordinary thing: as soon as I had stepped down and removed the noose, I had a clearer vision of my dementia. It came to me in the form of a dementia monster. I got home and decided to draw that monster. I thought if I gave it a face, I would take some of its power away. I was giving it an identity of my own choosing; I was in charge of him and not the other way around. So, I made it the ugliest, most unflattering shape I could. And now that my dementia monster had an identity, I felt I could move on. I had a past, but dementia wanted to take my future, so I had to do all I could to stop the shadows from engulfing my life and my future. This was my future and not one I was prepared to share with an intruder, especially one with such an evil face who had gate-crashed my life without permission.

I knew that this was not the best piece of art that anyone had done, but it meant something to me. At school I was a really good artist and there was still one of my paintings hanging in the corridor at my old school. Dementia had already taken away so much of me, including my ability to write and draw, but it was MY drawing and that was the important thing. That day I had taken my dementia monster by the scruff of its ugly, scraggly neck, held him up so his stupid little legs were dangling below him and eyeballed him. I told him that he would not always be in charge. If this dementia monster wanted a battle, then he was going to have one. I would not be defined by my dementia, but I would live alongside it and battle it all of the way. I felt myself drawing my body up so I stood taller. Suddenly, I had become a general on the battlefield of dementia, a warrior, ready for the fight ahead. My brain cells were my soldiers and I knew I would spend much of my time watching my soldiers fall. I knew I would be powerless on some days and have to watch the casualties fall from afar, watch them squirm and die and fade into nothing, but I also knew that there would be days when I was in charge. All of us with this condition were dementia warriors. We shone on the outside like towering beacons of light for all to see and yet inside we were dark and dull. Suppressing the shadows was what we did and we did it so very well. We were warriors, all of us!

And it was on this day, with my dementia monster facing me squarely, I knew I had won the battle and stood firm against the marauding dementia enemy. And let me tell you, there's not many folks on the timber yards in Suffolk who would put together a sentence like that! The most poetical I was likely to get whilst out in the woods felling trees was something like, "Hey, fella! That tree is doughy, will it hold a nail?" Here's a thing: one of the more curious parts of my dementia was that it had taken away my ability to write but enhanced my ability to express myself. These were the days when I say I have taken from my dementia, rather than it had taken from me.

I didn't tell Teresa what I had been going to do. I didn't see the point, although she knows now, and I often wonder what would have happened to her and Kate if the train hadn't been cancelled or I had jumped.

The other day when I was cycling with Deb, we were talking about this suicide attempt in terms of what to put in the book. And do you know, the feelings all came flooding back and I had to stop cycling and wipe my eyes. The emotion caught me totally by surprise and I was astonished that I still remember that day with such powerful emotions. What a thing to have contemplated; what a terrible thing I was driven to.

I said to Deb, "There are still the footprints of my boots on the tractor, you know. I think I had decided not to dust them off because I needed this reminder."

With my aborted suicide attempt came a new lease of life. I had decided that because there had been no one there to help me, my mission was going to be to help other people. I wasn't so arrogant as to think I was going to save lives or be the voice of dementia, because I was no one special; I never have been. But I wanted to do something to show that people like you, the people who were leaving the consultant's office with a new diagnosis or their families who were having to deal with this monster, or people like you who were living totally unaware of what was around the corner – and let's face it, it could be you – weren't alone. I wanted to do something to help and I wanted to give myself a sense of purpose in life.

One of the things I decided to do was to keep a journal of my life with dementia, but it didn't take long until the dementia monster snatched that idea away from me and ran, laughing and giggling at my frustration, back into his dirty, dark little corner. You see, my writing had deteriorated and finally became illegible. As a child I was ambidextrous and could write two different sentences simultaneously with both hands – this had been my party trick. Now I don't know if I am left-handed or right-handed. Now I can't even write my signature. If you think about it, our signature is such a necessary part of our lives and gives us access to so many things: banks, shops, entertainment. It is our stamp to define who we are; it is unique to us and if anyone forges our signature, we are affronted and our very identity is challenged. So, think what it is like not to have a signature. Think what it is like not to be able to write your signature in any consistent form. Whichever hand the pen is in, my brain just can't get the message to my hand to make the letters.

The first diary entry shows my handwriting in 2015 and the second shows the decline by 2017. That's a visual demonstration of how I lost that particular set of skills. Although I grin now when I see how, even then, I was determined not to let this grind me down and how that little smiley face somehow says so much in the way of my defiance.

The scary thing about losing my ability to read and to write more than one or two sentences also means that I will never read this book. I have to trust Teresa and Deb to make sure that it reflects my life and says the things I want it to say. I got to thinking about this and it is a bit like being in your own world where everything travels towards you and yet you are not in the loop anymore. I feel like I am in a different time zone, in a different world, and that others are in my world much more than I am. I suppose what I am trying to say is that, although this book is about my life, it is someone else's story because I will never read it. This makes me think about how vulnerable I have become and how I have to put my trust entirely in other people to protect me. If there are pictures in this book – and I hope there are some – then in a few years' time I will be able to look at the pictures and hopefully realise that they are of me but I still won't be able to remember doing the things that the pictures show me doing and I wonder if it will still feel like me. I hope that makes sense. You know, losing this ability to read is frustrating and makes me feel like a three-year-old at school.

Now, that has triggered a sudden clear memory! I remember we had a teacher who was cross-eyed and we never knew who she was looking at to scold. We called her 'north eye' and I swear she could look around corners. I remember her, poor old soul. But I don't really remember me anymore or even if I was the one that she was scolding.

Last year, in July 2019, quite by chance, I met Deb. We met in the local cycle shop. I do remember that! Without her support I don't think we would have sat down and written this book. I always knew I wanted to write a book about my condition, but there was no way I could have done this on my own. It was almost fate, the way Deb appeared.

Deb asked me why I wanted this book to be written. I think the answer is that it has created another purpose to my life. When you have dementia, you lose your ambition. Yes, you learn to live every day, but I think you lose your sense of achievement because you forget each day what you have achieved. It's like watering a dead plant: you just can't bring it back to life and so you give up trying. But if my life story and my achievements are written down, then at least they will be there and I hope that my plant will come back to life, even if only one or two leaves flower.

Just before my father died, I found him looking at his wedding photo taken sixty years ago. He recognised my mother, Betty, his wife, but he was struggling to recognise the strong young man who stood next to her. It puzzled him and it also scared him, I think, that he just could not remember who he was. And, of course, as my dementia progresses and I become more like Father, I also get scared. If you asked me to describe what I look like, I wouldn't be able to. I simply do not know what I look like anymore. Of course, if I look in a mirror, I recognise myself (and very dapper I am too, if I say so myself), so I am not as far down the dementia road as Father, but here's a thing, one day I will be – and one day there won't be a mirror shiny enough or large enough for me to recognise myself. I hope that this book will help me to remember who I was and not who I am because I am not sure I can deal with raw fear like that.

More and more these days, I think about Father and wonder how I will be if I live to his age. He was ninety-two when he died, although I sometimes do forget that he has died. The medication that I am on is the strongest dose available. Father never had a dosage like that, so I am clearly in a worse situation than he was, particularly if you think about my age.

In my mind I see dementia in three key stages. I think for older people – people like Father, who are further down the path of dementia – they are on the easy part of the path, the smooth path. They have accepted their destiny and allow themselves to slide along, subjected to the whims of other people, out of control, just existing. Other people make their decisions for them. I know that eventually I will have to succumb to dementia and when I have and can no longer fight, I will be on that path too but now, right now, I am on another stage, I am journeying up the rocky hard climb, still fighting, still me, still Peter and still a long way to travel before I reach the smooth path.

And then I think there is the final stage of the journey and this will be when I find myself living in an endless loop in time, not really understanding how I got to the smooth part, not remembering the rocky part and the fight I put up; not remembering from one day to the next, here but just existing and waiting. That scares me and that is why I focus on the here and now; on the things I can do and the things I am good at doing.

The other thing that happened as my dementia progressed was that I lost my ability to do maths, which meant I wasn't able to use money. That's another part of my life chiselled away as maths was a key part of my working life. I now have solved this problem by only using contactless cards, but it's just another unpleasant reminder of dementia's attempts to render you an incapable member of society. Bit by bit, dementia tries to remove your ability to function in life and I was having to come up with new strategies to cope.

When it became obvious that I couldn't write my thoughts down anymore I became despondent, but Kate suggested that I log my thoughts in a short video and post it on Facebook. So, I made a video and thought I would just do a couple or three, but before you knew it, I was doing a weekly video on living with dementia and getting amazing feedback from people all over the world. In one state in America, they use my videos to teach children what early onset dementia is and to take away some of those stereotypes. I find that amazing! Nearly two years later, by the time I got to video number 103, I made the decision to stop. It had become obvious to me that the act of making the videos had become too complex; I still had loads to say, but I just couldn't deal with the mechanics of recording and posting on Facebook and it made me very frustrated.

I asked Deb to post a message that the videos were stopping and the response was overwhelming. So, the compromise became that we would do a monthly update. I say 'we' because I just can't do these sorts of things on my own. I need support and, as hard as it is for me to recognise this and accept it, I have to. I can walk down my garden and get as far as my garden gate, but I can't push that gate open anymore because I don't know how to, and therefore I can't get through the gate to the other side. I can see the other side, which makes it all the more frustrating. The other side consists of a beautiful meadow where people stroll and enjoy life and see beyond their own home and experience new things, but it's a meadow which is not accessible to me anymore. The flowers in that meadow are not for me, the trees in the meadow – which I could still identify – and which tower over those below no longer include me in their shadows.

I now need people there with me, taking my hand and pushing the gate open for me. I have always been a proud man, always happy to lead the way, but I now realise that there is nothing wrong with needing help. The hardest thing is to acknowledge it.

Teresa and Kate were my main support, but sometimes I just didn't want them to know how hard things were. They lived with my dementia every day and I knew they needed the odd break and I still wanted to protect them for as long as I could.

So, with Deb's support, I started to make a monthly video update, and these have proved overwhelmingly popular. In a matter of hours of the updates being posted, they reached over four thousand people. I find this incredible to believe! They do seem to be a comfort for many other people. I remember sharing something on one of the earlier ones about how I always bit the inside of my mouth when I ate, always the left side of my mouth, and how painful this was. I had assumed that this was something that only happened to me, but so many people responded by saying this happened to them too and how reassured they were to know that others living with dementia experienced this too. Sharing this sort of information was invaluable and did provide reassurance or comfort for others out there.

In our dementia world, we always say that if you've seen one person with dementia, then you have only seen one person with dementia because everyone is affected differently by it. But what is the same, I am sure, is that our day-to-day lives are quite a struggle. But we improvise, we carry on, we live life to the best of our abilities, and I think that is something that people who don't have much connection with dementia should be made aware of. I am not the designated spokesman for those living with dementia, but I do want to say this on behalf of those living with the condition: it can be – no, it IS – a struggle. We try to fight this daily struggle inwardly, so from the outside it doesn't always give the impression that we are struggling. From the outside it looks as though the waters are pretty calm but, on the underneath, we are treading water and we are paddling like mad to keep our heads above the water level.

But here, with a little invention and support, I had suddenly changed. From being just a normal bloke in Suffolk, running a timber business, cutting trees, making orders, invoices, even dealing with the taxman (the less said about that, the better!), I had gone through the most incredible journey from diagnosis, depression, suicidal thoughts and two abortive attempts, and then a light shining on the path ahead and lighting up the next steps. I had a Facebook following, a YouTube audience, a brand-new website which Deb's husband, Martin, had created and a certain growing fame. It was up to me to take this further and to see what I could do. It was up to me to look at my dementia monster and say, "Come on then. You think you're hard? You think you're up to this battle?"

As I always say (apparently with some regularity), life isn't over with dementia; it's just a little different! And it certainly was going to be different from now on.

(iv)

So, having decided that I was going to make a difference in whatever time I had left, I hatched a plan. I had always been a keen cyclist and, in my youth, used to do cycling trials. I was quick and fit, and I still loved to cycle. When I used to do the trials, I would cycle in from Framlingham to Ipswich, which was fifteen miles, do the speed trial, eat a Mars bar and have a can of Coke, and then cycle home. I didn't have fancy cycling gear or electrolyte drinks or protein bars. I was just a good cyclist in a pair of baggy shorts and trainers. I do believe in different circumstances I might have been semi-professional. You know, the organisers of these time trials used to look at me and ask where my transport was and when I told them that I had cycled fifteen miles to get there, they always looked astonished. I was a skinny, raw-looking youth, but I believe I had a look of steely determination about me and give me a bike and I became a cycling demon!

As soon as my ability to drive our car deteriorated, I began to use my bike more and more. I had a 1950s Claud Butler which

I had bought for about £250 a few years ago. It was and still is a splendid bike. Riding it into our local town not only liberated me from the tyranny of dementia, it absolutely rekindled my love of cycling. And then, in one of those random moments, the idea came to me. I would raise awareness of this dreadful disease by cycling across the country – A to A (not A to Z, that would be too obvious). I chose Aberystwyth in Wales as my starting point (and not just because it was impossible to say and to spell!) and Aldeburgh in my beloved Suffolk as my finishing point. My plan was to prove that I was healthy, despite living with this dreadful condition, or at least I was healthy from my eyebrows down.

I knew that I couldn't do this challenge on my own, but the community rallied around me. Jon, who owned the local cycling shop, sourced me an excellent bike at a generously discounted cost with the understanding that we would publicise the make of the bike – so thank you, Moda! Adnams the brewery sponsored us, and local people were quickly on board to help out. Of course, I would need a cycling companion to help me with the route and to make sure I didn't cycle off in totally the wrong direction and end up in Torquay or John O'Groats. This companion quickly materialised, but I am not going to name her as, with just a couple of weeks to go, she withdrew from the challenge for personal reasons. However, it did mean that unless I found another person fit enough to cycle across the country, I wasn't going to be able to do the challenge, and all of the training and preparation would have been in vain. I was gutted and quickly slipped into a period of depression. What was the point, I thought? If I always had to depend on help, I was no better than a child. I was petulant and bad-tempered, behaving just like the child I felt I had become.

My daughter wasn't having any of this self-pity from her dad, though. Kate put out a plea on Facebook and, do you know, a total stranger from Kent answered that she would do the ride with me and, although we had never met before, she turned up in Friston with her bike, we piled bikes and ourselves into my brother's motorhome, he drove us to Wales and we cycled the entire challenge together.

My new friend, Jan, was my enabler. Jan's own husband was also living with Alzheimer's and so she had a great understanding of what support I was going to need and what role she was going to have to play. Some people said that it was like a busman's holiday for her, but it really wasn't. For Jan this was a wonderful release and an experience that I know she cherished. She was a great cyclist and was thrilled to be involved with this challenge. Despite living in Kent, Jan and I will remain lifelong friends and I am so grateful to her for stepping in at the last minute.

We cycled almost four hundred miles that week in the scorching sun and raised £6,000 for Young Dementia UK. Of course, we got lost, specifically around the Birmingham area, although apparently, I have been told that it's obligatory to get lost in Birmingham. In Birmingham, too, there are more canals than in Venice: I do remember the strangest facts in the cloudy haze of my dementia brain.

Some days we were so lost that we arrived at our hotel stop late and my wife would be worried and pacing the floor, but Jan was brilliant and kept me safe. Some days we had sweated so much and consumed so much water, but we still didn't need to use the toilets – that was how hot it was – and perhaps that's quite enough detail for this sort of book!

When we got back to Aldeburgh, we were greeted by a small, but noisy, crowd of people, the press and a bottle of champagne. A few cyclists from the League of Ordinary Riders were there too, to cycle the last few moments with me. The League of Ordinary Riders, in case you don't know, cycle on penny farthings. These bikes were called 'the ordinary' bikes when they were first constructed, and I suppose the sight of these ordinary bikes must have stayed in my head, because they made a reappearance not that long after I had finished this challenge.

I was on such a high! Although I did a lot of the planning, which I really enjoyed, I did have some help. I was beginning to learn to accept this and so many people had been involved in the planning of the challenge – especially Teresa and my old school friend, Norman, who drove the support car – that it gave me a sense of hope. I said before that I didn't want to be defined by my dementia. As I cycled over that week, I realised I was just the old Peter, doing what I did best. And that was a wonderful thing in my life at that moment in time.

This made me come to think about my life and I realised that, even though there were some things I could not do, and more things were going to be taken away from me by this dementia, there were still so many things I could achieve. I have always been a glass-half-full person and, as quickly as the dementia monster tried to empty my glass, the best way I could win was to fill it up again. I believe my successful challenge gave my monster a bit of a kick up the backside and he disappeared for a short while, skulking, coming up with a different way he could pin me down. But for that wonderful week, I reckon I was the victor. For those six days I became the man I used to be and not the man defined by dementia. I think this is so important for anyone, not just someone living with dementia, but for anyone with a life-changing or terminal condition. Remember back to the person you were, not the person you fear you might become. Make life about the 'I can do's, not the 'I can't do's.

CHAPTER
TWO
SUMMER 2018

DEB

(i)

SOUTH LONDON MEETS SAXMUNDHAM

When my husband, Martin, and I took early retirement in June 2018 and moved to the Suffolk market town of Saxmundham, we had no idea of what our future would hold and this was, in turn, both frightening and exhilarating. Saxmundham wasn't a place we had set our hearts on or scrimped and saved for years in order that we could live there. Truth to tell, we had never heard of Saxmundham. In fact, it took me a few weeks to spell (or even pronounce) Saxmundham properly.

Saxmundham was selected simply because:

- It was near the coast but not on the coast, as I don't like being woken up by early-morning squawking seagulls;
- It had a railway station (albeit with only one train an hour), thus facilitating trips down to London to watch Arsenal;
- It had a Waitrose;
- It had some coffee and cake shops and, probably most importantly of all…
- It wasn't South London.

And on such random factors are life-changing moments based.

Martin had worked for years in the computer industry, a job and a commute which was gently sapping the energy from him; I had worked with what were termed as 'troubled families' as a parenting practitioner in South London, and I was stale and cynical. When young people arbitrarily murder each other just because they feel 'disrespected', it does rather take away your faith in people's intrinsic goodness. I knew it was time to go.

We left South London – Southern Trains, smog, stresses, stabbings and senseless slayings – with all but a smattering of sadness and settled into our new home. I thought moving to Suffolk would bring a serenity and a wonderful change of life. And it has. But I had no idea it would bring with it the friendship of a man who has totally reshaped the way I see life and who has willingly flung open the doors to show me the view of his wonderful county and to his life in a way that has illuminated my days and changed my attitudes to living.

I'd heard about Peter before I met him. In my early days of living in Saxmundham, I spent a lot of time in Sax Velo, the local cycling shop, as it seemed to me a good community hub and the place where I might meet someone who might take pity on me and take me out cycling.

Caroline, who, along with husband Jon, owned the shop, told me that a local, a man called Peter Berry, had just returned from a cycle challenge, whereby he cycled all the way across the country.

Perhaps sensing my lack of wonder, or lack of geographical knowledge, she elaborated: "So, from Aberystwyth to Aldeburgh. On a bike."

"Impressive," I said.

But Caroline sensed I was not as impressed as I should be. "You do know he's got Alzheimer's?"

"Oh, right," I said.

I didn't really know anything about Alzheimer's. My elderly grandmother had been diagnosed with Alzheimer's in her seventies but my mother had protected me from her rages and mood changes. I only heard about the symptoms through the tiniest pieces of information my mother chose to share with me and so my knowledge was limited. I had just assumed that dementia was something that came with old age, like liver spots, false teeth, incontinence and irritability. I didn't know that younger people could be affected. And I certainly didn't know how.

"Yes, and he's only fifty-three."

I think I muttered some hugely inadequate platitude about how young that was.

"It's a terminal condition, you know. There is no cure."

I went home and thought about this briefly. Fifty-three did seem young to me, but then, caught up in my own personal quandary of life-changing decisions, Martin and I had a heated but fruitful discussion about how many toilet brushes we should buy for a house with four toilets. That age-old question, which had baffled and perplexed families for generations, reared its head: should we have one for each toilet or go for the less flamboyant but more sensible cost-cutting choice of the peripatetic toilet brush? You see, these were the issues which occupied us just over a year ago; these were the pre-Peter issues which bothered me and took up space in my mind. I thought no more of Peter and early onset dementia until the next day when I returned to the shop and made some throwaway remark along the lines of, "So, maybe I need to meet this great Peter Berry, the Suffolk cycling hero."

A slim, grey-haired, bronzed man, wearing full cycling gear, was standing in the corner inspecting the cycles. He turned to face me.

"Well," he said, "you've met him now." I could hear the Suffolk burr in his accent which made him sound warm and kind. He smiled and extended his hand. Peter put me at ease straight away and, although in hindsight, I really should have been embarrassed that I'd made a bit of a fool of myself by my pompous declaration, I really wasn't. I felt an immediate warmth towards Peter. He smiled like a man who loved life and people. How could this be a man living with a terminal condition? I'm not sure I would smile like that if it were me.

Mind you, to be honest, he didn't look as if he had dementia. This was my first erroneous assumption about those living with the condition and I shudder even now when I think back to that moment. What did I expect? A wild-eyed man with flowing unruly grey locks, drooling and dribbling into his bib, arms akimbo, running semi-naked, like a parody of King Lear, through the streets of Suffolk?

"I'm Deb," I said. "I've just moved up here. If you're ever free, maybe we can cycle together."

"Absolutely," he said. "And as you're new to the area, I can show you some great cycling routes."

I bumped into him a few moments later. Saxmundham is a small town. As well as boasting the cycle shop, the small, winding high street has a mixture of charity shops, estate agents, cafes and a butcher's shop, with the eclectic bonus of a framing shop and an art gallery, all of which seem to close mid-afternoon as if stuck in a touching time warp of old England. A walk along the high street, however slowly one might dawdle, only takes three minutes. So, when I saw Peter again, I waved and said, in the least original way I could muster, "Ah, the great Peter Berry. Fancy bumping into you again."

There was a moment of utter blankness across his face – it must only have been a fraction of a second – and then he smiled and said, "Hello again," but I realised in that instant that he had absolutely no recollection of meeting me, even though literally only a minute or two had lapsed. That cameo, that briefest of moments gave me the tiniest of glimpses into his world and the coping strategies he used. Peter was not going to admit that he did not remember me but he took his cue from me and realised that we must have met and only now, when I look back, I understand the courage it takes to keep up this façade and how being a showman and playing for his audience is so important for him.

And from such an unexceptional beginning, a friendship grew and my insight into the devastating world of dementia grew with it.

The thing about Peter and his dementia was that he opened doors for me, and my world grew as his was shrinking. He has made me challenge my own privileged perceptions of life, to realise that the things I moaned and complained about were too trivial for even a moment's thought, to make me realise that it was an irrelevance how many toilets, let alone toilet brushes, I owned. I came to realise that Peter very rarely complained. Generally, he was a glass-half-full person, and every time someone siphoned a drop from his glass, he found another drop with which to replenish it. I'm not so sure I could drink from such a glass as this without choking. I think the contents of the half-full glass would first curdle and then shrivel my insides. I fear that I would shower all those around me with vicious, stinging bile in an attempt to purge myself of the taste of dementia. But Peter gave the impression that he thrived on the contents of the half-full cup, that it nourished and sustained him, as it tasted so much better than the half-empty alternative.

True to his word, Peter took me out for a cycle ride. We got along well and we soon developed a routine of more regular rides, just Peter and me. Although he was part of a cycling group and also enjoyed solo rides, there seemed to be something about the dynamics of our friendship which appealed to us both. With every turn of the pedals, with every mile covered, a strange and wonderful friendship and interaction was developing.

(ii)

THE DEMENTIA MONSTER EXPLORED MORE FULLY

We haven't known each other long, but a fledgling synergy is forming between us. When we are out, I remind Peter to drink or to eat and he advises me about gears and hills. There is an equilibrium within this relationship which the heavy burden of dementia cannot unbalance. I would not be cycling without Peter, nor he without me.

Today we have cycled to Dunwich. It is the most spectacular countryside with views of the sea coyly, tantalisingly unfurling in front of us. We pause and admire the stunning array of colours, which, like a carnival's flags, are draped around Dunwich: purples, greens, reds and yellows flutter in the gentle summer breeze. It is one of nature's visual feasts; it tops up my soul and fulfils me. I believe it does the same for Peter.

There is something about cycling which prompts Peter to share his thoughts with me.

"Here's a thing," begins Peter. "You know, some time ago I gave my dementia an identity, and that way I could deal with it and move forward. I had a past, but dementia wanted to take my future so I had to do all I could to make sure the little bugger couldn't take this away. So, I drew my dementia monster, I created an identity for him and that's really helped."

"What does your dementia monster look like?"

"Oh, he's an ugly little bugger, a humpty-dumpty man with a pointy nose, dripping with snot. He's got evil eyes."

He looks at me and gives a half grin, as if to dilute some of the description.

"He's not got a lot going for him, really. When I go cycling, I leave my dementia monster at home. He's waiting for me, I know that. But when I'm out cycling, I'm in charge of my dementia monster, not the other way around. When I cycle, I constantly pedal away from the nothing which is all I see ahead of me and behind me. Cycling has become my salvation; my very heartbeat has become a turn of the pedals in my mind. You can only pedal forwards, not backwards, that's the important bit."

Peter's description of his dementia monster is so tangible it is as if I can feel the monster's hot, sour breath on my face. I half expect a tap on my back and a globule of green snot to creep down my shoulder. I glance at Peter. He is living in his moment again, looking at the scenery, listening to the sounds of the birds, just being. He is impervious to the drops of spittle and to the smell of the monster's acrid breath.

Peter turns and looks at me. "Does any of that make sense?"

I have come to realise that Peter's explanations are wonderfully vivid; every sentence contains a splash of colour. He paints a picture of his dementia, descriptive flecks splattered over a canvas, lighting up my mind, helping me to see what it might be like for him. When he talks it feels as if he is wiping the film of grease away from my vision of dementia and now everything in front of me sparkles with a crystal-clear clarity.

"It makes perfect sense," I say.

It is just another moment in time, encapsulating the burgeoning friendship; the two of us, leaning on our bikes, absorbing the scenery in front of us. It is as if I am seeing it for the first time and Peter, perhaps scared that he might be seeing it for the last time. But we are both aware of the shadowy, sinister presence of the dementia monster lurking on Peter's sofa at home, not with us, but close enough that I fear a corporal puff of wind will be all it takes to reunite the two of them.

"What does Teresa's dementia monster look like?" I ask curiously. In my mind I have already drawn a comparable figure: perhaps Teresa's monster is defined by sharp, jagged edges which pierce her heart when she looks at them; perhaps he is an evasive character, always ducking and diving, finding new ways to inflict pain on Peter; perhaps her monster is just an overweight piece of blubber which she hopes will simply explode one day and leave their lives, its discarded innards scattered over the road, to be consumed by the buzzards and hawks. I realise that my imagination is running riotous circles in my head.

Peter gives me a look, not of pity but almost of amusement at my naivety.

"Well, here's a thing: her dementia monster looks pretty much like me," he says. Yet he says it so kindly and with such compassion that a little part of my heart melts.

And, then, he climbs onto his bike, pulls back his shoulders and starts to pedal, just that little bit further away from his dementia monster but paradoxically, as our ride draws to its conclusion, we both know that each turn of the pedal also propels him back home and into the icy embrace of the dementia monster.

CHAPTER
THREE
AUTUMN 2018

PETER

(i)

NEW CHALLENGES

At this point during the autumn months, weather permitting, my days were mainly about cycling. I was still able to cycle on my own but gradually becoming aware that I didn't feel so secure and thinking to myself that I really needed to find a solution to this problem. Almost as if it was decided by fate, I had met an unlikely new friend a couple of months before. Deb and her husband, Martin, had come up from South London, and she soon became my cycling companion. I say unlikely because I'd never met anyone from South London before! Besides, I had always been a committed and contented solitary cyclist, but I now realised that I was more comfortable cycling with someone else, another indication of the progression of my dementia. It wasn't about having someone else to navigate or fix my bike and, let's face it, if it had been about this, I probably wouldn't have chosen Deb! Having once watched her try to work out which end of the pump to attach to the valve on the tyre, I quickly came to realise that her skills did not include anything remotely technical! But the main thing was, Deb seemed to understand my condition, albeit on a fairly superficial level at this point. Oh, and, of course, she was jolly good company and full of quips and jokes. That's the trouble with having a ghost writer; they slip all sorts of things into the text.

Things were also pretty good health-wise. I had decided not to have another scan. I didn't see the point. It wasn't like my brain was going to regenerate and who would want to know how much of a deterioration there had been over the last year? I knew and that was quite enough. I had no wish to look at an X-ray to have it confirmed. And I had no wish to have any more tests, or to go on any more drug trials. Teresa was keen for me to try as many trials as I could because she wanted to be doing something and I totally understood that. She was not the type of person just to stand by and watch. And I loved her for that, but, you know, I found the journey to Cambridge or to London very soul-destroying and I didn't want to waste any more time. I just wanted to use the good time that I had left to do the things which would make me happy and keep me stimulated.

The main thing was that I felt healthy physically. Teresa had always been one to try anything which might slow down the army on their determined dementia march. Now that I had decided to stop the drug trials, we had to create our own methods of combating the enemy. We focused on diet and exercise. We ate as healthily as we could and we cooked our meals together. And, although that was really important because it took us back to being just a normal couple, doing normal couple activities, there was also a bleaker side to this. It was also another way that I was able to chart the decline of my memory. When we first started to cook together, Teresa would write a list of instructions and I was able to go through the list slowly but carefully. So, I would happily be chopping onions, carrots, turnips – anything she put in front of me – and following my instructions. Gradually

I realised I was getting my carrots confused with my swedes and it's not every man who can say that. And then, even more painfully, I realised that I could only process one instruction at a time and then that one instruction had to be a verbal one. It was no good Teresa writing anything down for me, even though she put every instruction in its own box as, originally, that had helped with my reading and memory. Now it seemed that my memory was getting so poor that, by the time I read the instruction and returned to whatever it was I was meant to be chopping, I had forgotten what to do. But it was still a good thing to cook together as a couple and I would urge every couple to do this if at all possible.

A year or so ago, we decided we would become vegetarian. The way I saw it was like this: we were all responsible for our physical health as much as we could be. If we ate healthily and exercised, then we were doing as much as we could do to look after ourselves. I knew there wasn't much I could do about my brain, but I certainly was happy to take control of the rest of my body. I did notice the difference in how I felt, too, once I stopped eating meat. I also realised that I had become quite a sentimental old fool. Now that we had pigs in the field just by our garden, I couldn't begin to think about eating a bacon sandwich anymore. And because dementia had taken away my sense of smell, I wasn't even tempted to succumb to a bacon sandwich, which I believe is often the downfall of even the most determined vegetarian. Yes, I should explain: dementia had removed my sense of smell. That was another bizarre element of the condition. I suppose my brain was working out what I needed and what I could cope without and it decided that I just didn't need to smell anything anymore. When Teresa cooked, she always asked how the food smelled and I always said it smelled great, but I hadn't smelled the cooking smells, the onions, the garlic – things we all took for granted – for many months now.

Oh, now here was another thing: Deb reminded me that a few weeks ago, when we were out having coffee, a woman walked by our table and apparently, I stopped listening to Deb, turned my head and said I could smell this woman's perfume. I had told Deb this in astonishment because it was the first time for months that I had been able to smell anything. It took me back; it connected me to other people in a way which had been removed. I obviously don't remember this now, but Deb had written it down for me on my Facebook page and many people had commented on how wonderful this was and at that moment, living for that moment in time, it must have been an immense sensation for me to experience again. I asked Deb to include this incident in the book because many people are not aware that certain senses are wiped out by dementia.

Generally, though, I was feeling healthy, but because of being so acutely aware that I was becoming more forgetful, I knew I needed another challenge to keep me going. I needed something to focus on. Some of the euphoria from the recent cycle challenge had died down by now. There were many things which kept me occupied and busy – and, I suppose, relatively content. I enjoyed pottering in the garden, keeping it neat and tidy, and I took pleasure from cutting the grass. I also loved to chop wood for the wood burner and these things did make me content and give me a sense of purpose. But I have always been the type of man who needs a target to focus on. And never more so than now.

And then, one Sunday, when Deb had gone cycling with the Sunday cycling group from Saxmundham, she had a fall from her bike and broke her shoulder. I had left her alone in the company of other cyclists and she came back to me all broken! That should be a lesson for her! Of course, I was distressed for her, but her accident also impacted on me in a way which surprised me and I was left to cycle on my own again. But, you know, it was not the same at all. The process of solitary cycling scared me, not because I didn't know my way around, because I still did – although there were increasing moments when I went blank, but then I would simply follow the national cycle routes and the problem would be solved. No, it was more because if I did get lost, I was worried that I would freeze and just become confused and disorientated, and I did not want that at all. I did not want to have my dementia rammed into my face like that. Cycling was what made me Peter Berry and there was no place for my dementia monster when I was out cycling. Cycling was everything, but getting lost and disorientated would be an open invitation for the monster to sneak his way back into my world.

As I have said, when I cycled, I left my dementia at home. But inevitably, when I returned home after several hours' cycling, things changed. I had a routine: I cleaned my bike, showered, lit the wood burner so the house was toasty and warm, and then I would sit on the sofa, enjoying the remainder of the endorphin rush and the memory of feeling like the old me.

This would be the point when my dementia monster might well decide to edge his way towards me, to snuggle up a bit, to nudge himself closer to me, to remind me he was still there. I was powerless to stop him. Although my escape was short, it was very fruitful and so I learned to live with my monster's presence. His and my silence were the proof of that. Acceptance and contentment were mine again, despite his presence and the sense of his hot breath on my face.

The other weird thing was, in a way which I find difficult to explain, it just felt right, cycling with Deb and, equally, it felt wrong to cycle without her! One thing about Deb when she cycled was how often she sniffed! I grew very fond of those sniffs and didn't want to cycle in a sniff-free zone. Deb always seemed to run out of tissues when we were out, so it got that I carried extra tissues around with me and produced them for her, like a magician produces a rabbit from a hat.

When she wasn't sniffing, we would talk as we cycled, but sometimes, we also just pedalled in a quiet, contented silence. The thing about cycling was that it allowed me to be the man I used to be; as I pushed down on those pedals, my dementia decreased, and I felt stronger and in control. I knew that dementia was stripping me of myself, but I also knew that, when I cycled, when I pushed myself physically, I became more than I ever was. It was hard to explain, but it almost was as if I was a larger, more capable person than I had been before. When I cycled, I was the master and dementia was the slave, albeit for a short while. These cycle rides with Deb had become unexpectedly important to me and to my well-being.

But now she was moping around Saxmundham with her arm in a sling and our cycling days were temporarily put on hold. Her depression at her own inactivity oozed into my life and I was in danger of becoming equally lethargic. I knew I had to find something to do, something to focus on, whilst she was incapacitated. And so, I decided to plan my new cycle challenge. The first part was easy. I decided I was going to cycle four of the counties of East Anglia: I would start in Suffolk, go to Cambridgeshire, into Lincolnshire, then Norfolk and home to Suffolk. I got out the map and made marks on various places which looked like sensible stopover points, but then I stumbled upon that gate at the bottom of my garden and, push and grunt as I might, I could not open it and I could not go beyond it. I was simply unable to plan beyond this point. It was so unfair: I knew there was a world out there, yet it was simply beyond my ability to access it.

I was cross and so, in order to compensate for the lack of my ability to plan, I decided to make the ride that little bit more challenging for me. I decided I would raise the bar that little higher. Making it harder was my way of proving to myself that I was still supremely capable in many ways and that, by focusing on the positives, I was able to ignore the negatives.

My solution? I would cycle the whole ride on my penny farthing. Years ago, I had raced penny farthings in velodromes and I knew I had been able to ride them competently. As I said before, at the end of last year's challenge I had borrowed an ordinary bike (as penny farthings were called) and had a brief cycle. I think that must have stayed in my head when I made the decision to ride the new challenge entirely on a penny farthing.

A friend from the League of Ordinary Riders lent me a penny farthing to try out and it was like I had never been away from one. There are no brakes or gears on a penny; to mount it, you push along and scoot up via a small step onto the saddle. It requires balance and strength, and I had both. To dismount, the reverse process kicks in. I always say that it took a few hours to master how to mount and dismount a penny farthing but several months to ride it safely. I loved the bike I practised on and so I bought it. That was the good thing about living with dementia; you knew you didn't have time to waste in making decisions. So, here is a message, a reality check for everyone out there, not just those of you living with a terminal condition, but for everyone. If you want to do something (and it's legal and affordable), then I would urge you just do it! What's the point of planning and wondering? We just don't know what the future holds.

The wonderful thing about riding a penny farthing was that it was an old skill which quickly came back to me.

Although this was a relatively new bike (seven years old) it was still the most beautiful penny farthing. If you can fall in love with a bike – and I think I have proved that I could – then Penny was certainly one to capture my heart. Bike purchased; challenge created. Now I just needed a mended cycling partner to train with me! I had started to refer to Deb as 'sticky-outy Deb', because a piece of bone from her shoulder seemed to be stuck at an angle; you could have hung your coat on the bone that protruded out of her shoulder. So sticky-outy Deb needed to get fixed and to get fixed quickly. No time to waste! We had a challenge to train for!

My original plan had been to cycle the challenge and to encourage others with life-changing or terminal conditions or even depression to climb on their bikes at various points along the route and to cycle some of the journey with us. I had hoped they would donate £5 towards Young Dementia UK to participate, but for me it was more about raising awareness and to show the world that a little physical exercise could go a long way in making people feel better. If I encouraged just one person to take up cycling or any other exercise as a result of this challenge, well, I thought that would be a job well done.

But the whole thing snowballed to an extent which both surprised and excited me. The wonderful thing about living in a small town, as we did, was the feeling of community. It really does exist, so don't let anyone tell you it's a myth. Other people in Saxmundham, including an old school friend (Mark) with whom I had lost touch but who found me on Facebook, decided that they would like to do the challenge with me for its entirety, and then Jan, my cycling saviour from Kent, also said she would like to do it. Suddenly we were a team of five – Mark, Jan, Mike (another local cycling enthusiast), Deb and me – and I knew that other people from the local cycling group would join us at various stages. The four counties cycle challenge was in full swing!

A lot of time in the autumn was spent in either planning the challenge or seeing Deb and tolerating her showing me the sticky-outy bone in her shoulder (and anyone else in the area who would look at it). One thing about Deb and her shoulder – she was not shy about displaying it to most of Saxmundham. We really did spend a great deal of time in our local bakery, chatting, eating cake and getting to know each other that little bit better. And as we chatted, I allowed a little more of my dementia fears and thoughts to seep out because it felt important to spread the message and Deb had mentioned that she would like to write about my story. The moment had come!

DEB

(ii)

LIVING IN THE MOMENT

Alas, the inevitable is destined to happen when a clumsy person, like me, rides a bike too fast and doesn't pay attention to the surroundings, more specifically the kerb. Soon after buying my new bike, I hit the kerb, flew off the bike, landed on my shoulder and broke my clavicle and scapula. These are not parts of my bike, but, as I am to discover, fairly important parts of my body. I am sprawled out, motionless and in pain, on the damp, cold pavement in Felixstowe for forty minutes, waiting for the ambulance. My cycling friends all wait with me and also in attendance are three firefighters, a nurse and several concerned locals. Apparently, I have fallen just by the fire station where the firefighters are doing a health and safety course and I provide a welcome and practical release from the tedium of study and, although I am reliably informed that they are young and muscular firefighters, from my semi-recumbent position on the ground I can only see their knees.

I manage to mutter, "What's the Arsenal score?" before succumbing to the painkiller and sinking into a relieved semiconscious knowing we have won 5-1. I finally arrive in Ipswich A&E, bloodied, bowed, confused but still functioning, with a diagnosis of a broken shoulder and a directive not to exercise for weeks.

For me, this is the worst thing that could happen. I am an impatient, slightly hyperactive person and hate being incapacitated, even though rationally I know it is only for a matter of months and not forever.

There is the brief moment when I can untangle my own selfish thoughts and I am able to think about what life might be like for Peter, who at some point will have to face a life whereby he is incapacitated, but then, intrinsically self-centred as I am, my thoughts return to my own plight.

During this time Peter becomes a great support to me. Forget anyone who says that I am supporting Peter. Our friendship is developing into a mutually supportive one that, I think, surprises and pleases us both.

We start to meet daily for coffee and a chat. Today Peter is very animated. He has come up with his latest challenge, which is to cycle on his penny farthing across four counties, and he tells me he will not do it unless I do the whole challenge with him. He is very persuasive and, even though I have my broken shoulder and can't imagine cycling ever again or even looking at my bike, I agree that I will join him.

During this time, it is Peter who reassures me I will get better, that I will go cycling again and that all will be well. It is Peter, the man with a terminal condition, who finds the inner strength and emotional ability to step outside his own life to look at mine and tell me that I will get better. At the time I am so engrossed in myself, that I do not realise what a giant gesture this is.

Rationally, of course, I know Peter is right. My shoulder will be healed by a skilled orthopaedic surgeon and I will be nursed back into good health and all that will be left is the tiniest of scars and a small protuberance of bone. I will have sympathy and people will wait on me and I will feel special. And then, in two months, I will be cycling, running and swimming. Two months! That's all. Yet as I heal, a little more of Peter's brain will have died. As I heal, Peter will have edged a little closer to face his dementia monster. As my bone knits together, more of Peter's brain cells will blacken and die. I chide myself for wallowing in my self-indulgent depression.

Having shared with me his plan to do the four counties challenge, Peter suddenly becomes a little more serious.

"Well, here's a thing," he says.

I am learning that this is one of Peter's favourite phrases and generally precedes something which blows me away.

"We've got the challenge to plan and to look forward to. That's great. But you know, so many things are being removed from me. Not just my ability to remember, but I feel as if more and more of me being an adult is being taken away. Sometimes I feel like a child. When we go out, Teresa chooses my food because I just can't read the menu these days. It overwhelms me. I can't remember any more what food I like and what food I don't like, although olives are most definitely the devil's food. Teresa leaves me notes – cut the vegetables, turn the oven on, put the casserole in the oven. Do the hoovering, do the dusting. She's not nagging me at all – she has to write it all down for me, otherwise we'd never eat – but I feel more and more of me is being taken away."

He pauses. I know there is more coming. I have come to recognise the Peter Berry sense of theatre. A drum roll will most assuredly not be out of place now.

"We had a letter in the post the other day about another brain scan."

"And?"

"And I have decided not to have one. Teresa would like me to. But I just don't want to. I don't see the point. It's not like it's going to have improved, is it? And I don't want to know how much more of my brain has died."

Of course, Peter must hang on to some decision-making capacity because I can see he is in danger of becoming as infantilised as he fears. There is a quiet desperation about how he clings to his remaining autonomy, his fingertips whitening as he clings harder each day. But I am sad, for him and for Teresa, that they are faced with this terrible choice. I wonder what I would do in his position.

I think about my broken shoulder again. *How strange*, I think. With my shoulder I actively want to see the X-rays and scans, I want to see the broken bone because I know it will be fixed. I have even got a picture of the X-ray on my phone to show to the few unsuspecting friends who have not yet been subjected to viewing the injury. Part of me enjoys the special and sympathetic reactions I get from people when I force them to see my 'sticky-outy bone'.

But, in the same way as Peter does not want to tell people he is living with dementia, he also has no desire to see his own broken mind. What an antithetical pair we are. As openly as I flaunt my temporary disability, Peter desperately conceals his permanent one from others and now, it would seem, from himself. He does not want to see the black parts of his brain which are dying off and to know that he is edging closer to dementia's next evil chapter and its ultimate, inevitable conclusion. He does not want to be reminded of his decline and his mortality. The juxtaposition between our attitudes and ailments is stark and, if I'm honest, gives me a much-needed sharp kick in the ribs. But, luckily, it avoids my shoulder. I don't think I could have coped with that.

Peter says, "Well, there's no point worrying about the future. I won't be part of anyone's future," and it is said without a shred of self-pity. He has looked at self-pity – the same self-pity that I am lugging about with me all day – and booted it contemptuously into touch.

When I look up to thank him for the reality check, he is tackling his mountain of cakes and coffee (sometimes he forgets what he has ordered and just has cakes stacked up in front of him like shots of vodka in a bar) and I can see he has already moved on. The conversation we have just had has already gone for Peter, but it has not gone for me. It's in my head, tapping at my memory almost in double time as if to compensate for Peter's lack of memory. He has said to me that the door to his long-term memory has long since been slammed shut and there is no room for anything else in there; the door to his short-term memory has pretty well been demolished and the contents of the room been vacuumed up, devoured by the same evil monster which is sucking up his brain cells.

As always, Peter is just living for this moment, for the sweetness of the cakes and the buzz of the caffeine (and, unless I am deluded, for the pleasure of the company), and I admire him for this and tell myself to clamber out of my pit of self-indulgence.

So, you see, even in our early days of getting to know each other, Peter has bestowed on me a wonderful gift and is teaching me a valuable lesson. He is teaching me to try to live for the moment. And what a gift this is. I want to reach out and clutch it to me and never let it go, but I find this so very hard to do. I am always searching for something – don't misconstrue me – I am content, I am fortunate – but I always wonder if there is more to life than I have or I fear that perhaps tragedy is just around the corner, waiting to trip me up. I am a catastrophiser of the highest order. I find it hard to enjoy what I have; my mind always races on to the next event in my life. The single, special moment which Peter, because of his dementia, is forced to live for and cherish has always eluded me.

AUTUMN 2018

As I reflect on my life, I get the sense that I have been waiting for someone to tell me this: live for the moment. I have been searching for someone who is living proof that this is the only way to exist. I have spent a lifetime grumbling, moaning, looking for something, and now I have been enlightened by Peter; he has provided me with this unexpected gift. It might not be beautifully packaged with a bow or ribbons and it might not be extravagantly presented to me and it might not have had a cute kitten gift card attached to it and, indeed, he might not even know that he has given me this, but, to me, and for my sticky-outy bone, it is a gift and the timing is perfect and I am grateful indeed.

63

PETER

(iii)

*THE FOUR COUNTIES CHALLENGE TAKES SHAPE,
MY BRAIN LOSES MORE SHAPE*

As the planning for the challenge progressed, I realised how much my condition had deteriorated. I found it difficult to play any active role in organising our challenge. I couldn't book the hotels for the overnight stays, I couldn't work out the lunchtime stops, I couldn't really work out the timings involved each day. The only thing I knew with any certainty was that I would be cycling about fifty miles a day on a penny farthing. To be honest, I could barely remember the counties we were going to be cycling through. It was a real measure of how much my condition had deteriorated: last year's challenge I would say was one where I definitely had my finger on the pulse; this year's challenge I could barely place my hand around the wrist. I just had to rely on the team around me and I found this hard to accept. The challenge excited me and yet the planning depressed me; that was the strange thing. I wanted to focus on the challenge, but at the same time, I tried to not think too much about it because I did not want a reminder of how much things had changed from last year, when I planned the bulk of the challenge myself.

Sometimes it was the smallest of details which irked me. I remember, we were out in a cafe one day, when someone said to me, "Oh, you're Peter Berry, the guy suffering with dementia." He meant no harm; it was a comment borne out of curiosity and ignorance rather than malice, but when I heard those words it cut right into me. I tried to see myself through others' eyes and the image which I saw was of an old duffer, tottering around helplessly, perhaps trying to mount and ride a bike. The image was pathetic, laughable, and I hated it. Just hearing that one word – 'suffering' – made me sad for myself but also for others. If this was how they saw someone living with this condition, well then, there was a lot of education still needed to be done. I remember catching Deb's eye (she looked as horrified as I felt at the unfortunate phrase) and I pointed to myself and mouthed, "That's me, you know," and, bless her, she tried so hard not to giggle, but a sort of muffled snort came out. It was moments like that when I knew she 'got it', that I could trust her and that I could start to talk to her much more freely and let her into my dementia world.

A few weeks into the planning process, Jan contacted my wife. She had fallen off her bike and had broken ribs and sustained other injuries, so would not be able to do the challenge with me. What was it with these women and their inability to stay upright on the saddle of their bikes?!! When Teresa told me, I was really upset, but worse than this was that I kept forgetting Jan was hurt. I believe this threw up a problem for Deb and the others, who couldn't decide whether or not to tell me every time I mentioned Jan's name and that she was going to be part of the group. The simple answer? Use your judgement and, if it is appropriate, then be honest with people living with dementia. If there is nothing gained by the honesty, then a little white lie is fine. But for me, at this point in my journey, I needed to be told about Jan and it was up to me to cope with my own emotions. I am not a child and, although sometimes it felt as if people treated me as a simpleton or as a child, I was an adult able to deal with things that other adults dealt with and to take responsibility for how I felt. It was only my memory which was being removed, not my emotions or my soul.

I do have to admit, though, sometimes it was hard to keep a cheerful face to those around me. I would not let them know how hard it was for me. I would not show my true feelings. Only Teresa, and perhaps now occasionally Deb, saw how much I struggled to project this image of cheerfulness.

Over the last couple or three years, I had been called a showman because no one really knew I was living with this condition. I had managed to deceive people and that pleased me. But when people found out, their attitudes changed. There was a moment when Teresa and I were in the supermarket (more than one moment, actually, as she did seem to spend an inordinate amount of time there!) when a lady came up to us. I couldn't remember her name and she obviously realised this and so – and this was true – she turned to face Teresa, away from me, and said to Teresa, quite loudly, "How's Peter getting on with his dementia, then?" as if it was a new car or something which I was going to return when I'd had enough of it, as if I was just trialling it for a while until I got fed up with it. I felt like saying I was getting on just fine with it, although I feared it needed a new clutch, but I kept quiet. It wasn't her fault; of course, she was concerned but, along with her genuine concern, she also carted an unopened box of ignorance with her in her shopping trolley and took this occasion to share it with us down the tinned fruit aisle. I realised that people really did need educating and an idea started to form in my head about how I was well placed to raise people's awareness of what it was like to live with dementia.

Actually, people's ignorance, embarrassment or awkwardness was something which I had noticed more and more. Some people were simply embarrassed to talk to me. If I had been diagnosed with cancer, I do believe they would have come up to me and asked how I felt or asked how the treatment was going. They would have looked me in the eye and seen me, Peter, bravely battling cancer. That's what they call people with cancer – battlers, fighters. I don't think I've ever heard people describe me and my dementia in those terms. We are most definitely 'sufferers' in their eyes. People would have communicated with me because I was still Peter. But with dementia, they assumed I was not able to talk for myself and that somehow, I was no longer Peter. Everything went through Teresa. I wanted to tell them that I had only lost thirty-eight per cent of my brain capacity and was still more than able to communicate with them, but here's the rum thing: people seemed downright embarrassed to communicate with me. We also lost a lot of our friends; they just drifted away as if dementia was contagious and they feared they might catch it from me. Or perhaps they just weren't sure of how to cope with me and were thinking ahead and didn't think they could be around us when my condition deteriorated. I honestly don't know people's motives, but I do know that we became socially quite isolated. On top of everything else Teresa and I had to deal with, this felt like the final hammer blow for us.

When my mother-in-law referred to my dementia she tended to say, "Peter's got something wrong with his brain," but I honestly don't think she ever really believed I was living with this condition or she certainly didn't understand the full extent of it.

Just after my diagnosis, when we were gradually letting people know that I was living with this condition, Teresa was out shopping. She came home really upset. She said she bumped into someone who – meaning well, as people generally did – felt entitled to give her take on the situation. Apparently, this woman had suggested to Teresa that I might be putting it on, to avoid work, perhaps. After all, I looked perfectly well in myself. If I had just tried a bit harder, she suggested, I could have shrugged this problem off; normal life would have resumed and Teresa wouldn't have been under so much pressure. Teresa said that it felt as if she was angry with me for being ill, as if I had let Teresa down somehow, as if my dementia was an inconvenience for her, rather than a life-changing terminal condition.

I came to the conclusion that dementia was not the thing which robbed us of our dignity, but it was the reactions of others which did.

So, to counteract this, almost like my own personal challenge, I tried really hard to present as 'normal'. I devised strategies to get around the fact that, oftentimes when we were out, I simply did not remember people, either their faces or their names. The game was for me to make them think I did. When I couldn't remember someone's name (and this was now more often than not) I would substitute something neutral like 'my friend' or 'my man'; when I had no idea of context or what people did for a job, I would say something like, "Are you still in the same line of work, then?" and then I would pick up on the clue they might have given me. Now that I am further down my journey, I don't make so much pretence to hide the fact that I don't know who I am talking to and I have learned simply to say, "Sorry, remind me who you are," and laugh to show that I don't care at my appalling lack of memory, even though I do, but then it's really important to put on this act.

I saw myself and my dementia as two separate things. We walked a parallel path and we could see each other very clearly, but at this point we were separated by a flowing river. I knew that I had to keep to my path with the river between us. As long as I stayed to my side of the river, all would be well. Once the two paths converged, then I would be swept away in the river and I would never get back onto my path. If I could convince other people or deceive other people that I was 'normal', then in my mind I felt that I kept to my side of the path for that little while longer. That's why Teresa called me a showman. Only she really knew how hard it was to put on this show. Eventually I told Deb, but my pride meant that I really didn't want people to know. I was Peter the Showman. Not Peter living with dementia. It was another little victory for me; I chalked it up on the victory sheet and shoved it in the face of my dementia monster and laughed at him, even though, one day, I knew he would laugh back at me but longer and harder.

So here I was, smiling and laughing with the world; here I was, happy, jolly Peter who incidentally was living with a terminal condition but, hey, that wasn't going to bother Peter. Happy Peter was everyone's friend, always a quip on my lips and a joke. Happy Peter did not want to push his dementia onto other people. Happy Peter had a fixed smile which, if you looked carefully, was as hollow as a chocolate Easter egg and would melt at the first exposure to the sun's rays.

DEB

(iv)

PETER, THE SHOWMAN

We are sitting, as we frequently do, in the bakery – ah, where would we be without our lovely local bakery! My shoulder is on the mend. I have had the luxury of making the decision not to have surgery. Instead I have decided to live with a perpetually broken shoulder because it seems to me that the surgery presents more negatives than positives. My shoulder is functional, if somewhat aesthetically unpleasing to the purists who might prefer their shoulders not to have a piece of bone sticking up. But I have made a choice to suit me. How fortunate am I? Whilst our conditions are not comparable, I am keenly aware that I had that choice and that Peter has never had a choice about what to do about his condition.

We are going to cycle next week as the first step in preparation for the cycle challenge. It will be our first ride for a couple of months and Peter will cycle on Penny and I will use my road bike again. I am excited and nervous, and my mind is on me rather than Peter. But, in true Peter fashion, he grabs my attention with his words.

"Here's a thing," he says. "I look like a shop front with all sorts of gleaming, wonderful things in the window. Outside my shop, there's planters with colourful flowers, and a well-maintained pathway leading to the shop. The windows are clean and shiny, and the paintwork freshly applied. It looks like the sort of shop you would want to visit. It's a great shop full of exciting things to buy and look at."

Like a surgeon examining his patient, Peter studies his gingerbread man for a moment and then, with great precision, extracts a button from its midriff and pops it into his mouth. His enjoyment is apparent and crystallised for a transient moment, before it is gone forever.

"But in reality," he continues, "once you go into my mind and start to rummage around, what you get is the rubbish in the back of the store, untidy and messy, full of cobwebs. It really needs someone to sort through it. It's unusable goods, you see."

Peter isn't looking for sympathy; he eschews pity. He is merely trying to explain to me what it is like to be him and to live with dementia. He has no expectation that I tell him it will be all right because, clearly, it will not be and I will not belittle him by meaningless epithets or reassurances.

And so, on this unremarkable day, we sit, Peter and I, two friends in a comfortable bubble of companionship, just being, just living in the moment as he has taught me to do. Apart from thinking about our training for the challenge and discussing where we might cycle to, there is nothing particular to say and it doesn't really matter. I feel held, contained, knowing Peter will devise a route for the training and that he will look after me and my bike (preferably, but knowing Peter's love of bikes, not necessarily in that order). I feel safe in Peter's company.

This moment of serenity is broken when the man at the next table leans over and taps Peter's arm.

"Peter! Great to see you again."

"You too, my friend," replies Peter. His face instantly breaks into a huge beam.

"It's been a long while!"

"Too long," agrees Peter.

"How are you?"

"Wonderful, perfect. As ever."

There then follows a lengthy conversation in which Peter participates fully and enthusiastically.

"Who was that?" I ask when the man leaves.

"Do you know what?" says Peter solemnly. "I have absolutely no idea whatsoever." And, suddenly, even as we both laugh, I see it, there it is, that embryonic moment of sadness, gone before it has time to form fully, hidden away from his audience, to be replaced by a broad grin: Peter the Showman at his best.

Giving the dementia monster an identity was key to Peter being able to leave the monster at home and begin to take charge of the dementia

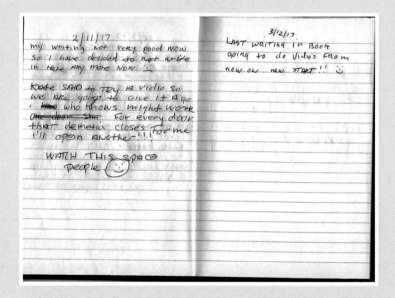

30/8/15

This is a memory that I am writing down just in case it goes away:-

When I was about 12 years old I went with Father to look at some tree work along Blaxhall Rail Line it was a very hot day and had been a hot summer (1976). We walked along the line it was moving in the heat (shimmering) there was animal bones all along the line, as we walked we could hear a train coming up the line, we could feel the track vibrating, my Father put a 2p bit on the track and we stood back a bit and watched the train go passed, after it had gone we found the coin it had been flattened but the train wheels! I still have it today ☺.

3/9/15

Good day today (clear day all day ☺). I am finding it difficult to read things and take in what I have read, I have noticed this more and more seemt like what I read doesn't seem to stay in my head, reading little bits is best (oh well carry on), another day tomorrow!!!

Last few days have quite good clear days so more good days than bad ones! can't be bad then (what's all the fuss about then!) lets see how it all goes.

7/9/15

At night time I sleep well at first until about the early hours of the morning then my mind is full of things, thoughts that don't make any sense my mind keeps me

Peter's diary in 2015. The writing is clear and neat

2/11/17

my writing not very good now so I have desided to not write in here any more now ☺

Kate said to try a viello so we are going to give it a go who knows might work For every door that demetia closes for me I'll open another!!!

Watch this space
people ☺

3/12/17

Last writing in book going to do vidios from now on new start!! ☺

By 2017 the deterioration in Peter's handwriting is apparent

Great contrast of my road bike and Peter's penny farthing

Peter looking suitably casual by Penny

Peter riding Penny through Woodbridge during training

*The look of joy and triumph on Peter's face is evident as he crosses
the finishing line after his Four Counties Challenge*

*We finish the 1,500-mile Alzheimer's Research UK challenge
with the traditional pose*

Peter and Teresa in 2020

Peter reflects on the challenges just gone … and the challenges ahead

PETER

(V)

AWARENESS RAISING

It was extraordinary. I wouldn't have said that I had become a celebrity, far from it, but I was certainly becoming more of a known figure in Suffolk. Some of that was probably due to the fact that I spent a lot of time on Penny and this created quite a stir in our little towns around Suffolk. I didn't think there would be many other men with a diagnosis of dementia cycling around for miles on a penny farthing bike. In fact, I was prepared to swear to it!

But the other thing which really started to take off were my videos on Facebook. I started to acquire a bit of a following and my weekly updates were watched by people, not just from the United Kingdom but as far away as India, America and New Zealand. Kate also uploaded them all on YouTube and I discovered many people – over six hundred – subscribed to my YouTube channel. It seemed that people really wanted to hear what I had to say. And having lived with Teresa and Kate for all those years, that notion was certainly a bit of a novelty and one to savour!

I was also contacted by a range of dementia organisations in Suffolk, all of whom were trying to push the dementia agenda forward but, as we had found when we were first diagnosed, many of their activities just didn't really suit us. But I was glad that things were moving forward for others, if not for me, in that respect.

Anyway, as a result of this increased publicity, I started to receive invitations to give short presentations about living with dementia to relevant organisations and social workers.

I was more than happy to do this, but I don't really remember the people I spoke to now. I have relied on Deb to jog my memory as she writes my story.

One day we cycled down to Thorpeness to speak to a group of people from an organisation called PROBUS. These meetings were for retired businessmen from the area who met and had lunch together and then were 'entertained' by an after-dinner speaker. I was happy to attend – who said there was no such thing as a free lunch!

I cycled down on Penny whilst Deb was on her road bike. We sat and ate lunch, and then I spoke for about thirty minutes. Deb assured me that no one fell asleep and that I got a rousing reception when I finished speaking. I suppose that talking about dementia to a group of older people would have resonated with them. One of the questions was, "How do you know that you have dementia?" This was a common question that people had and I think people generally were really worried that this was the path that they were destined to go down. I was happy to explain that dementia was not about forgetting things temporarily but about a whole cloud of confusion which squeezed your brain and made some things just disappear permanently from your memory banks.

I explained that dementia was something that changed your whole outlook on life. For me, my world with dementia, was a much smaller space. Pre-dementia days, which seemed like a distant past now, when I used to talk with people, when I really used to have proper conversations with them about current affairs or television programmes or social issues, it felt like these conversations were painted on a landscape in wonderful colours. Now, with my world shrinking, it felt as if that vast landscape was no more than a small plot of land. The vivid colours of the landscape had faded into sepia and the world I inhabited was now dull and colourless. I wasn't able to watch television or to read a book or to listen to the radio. My world was shrinking more rapidly than I cared to imagine.

I explained that dementia meant that, when I was stimulated, when I had to try really hard to be 'normal', my brain lit up like a Catherine wheel and exploded into colour, but it would quickly return to a sad sparkler, shining briefly before fading and being extinguished. I loved the days when my world was full of colour, but by the evening I was drained and back to the flickering, almost-extinct sparkler which I keep clenched in my hand until its last moment because I don't want it to go out. Ever.

I explained that dementia was about those of us living with the condition being forced to build our own shelters from the dementia storm, the storm which you knew was approaching with the passing of each day and the storm which was going to knock you down eventually. We built our own shelters because others did not realise how strong the shelter had to be. And we took refuge in those shelters like wounded animals when the storm clouds gathered, only venturing out when the sun was shining again.

I explained that dementia meant that I was forced to walk a narrow, rocky, dark dementia path that demanded 110% of me not to stumble, because once I stumbled, I feared I would not stand again.

That was my dementia world. Take it or leave it.

So, these talks were a great opportunity to explain to people what my world was like, to take them into my world but then to release them back into their own world because I wouldn't wish them to stay permanently in such a dark place. But the talks also enabled me to show my penny farthing off and explain the challenge, and we started to generate publicity this way.

Another talk I gave was to a group of social workers whose job was to work with those living with dementia. Again, I have to rely on what Deb has told me, but apparently those in the room were totally absorbed by the things I had to say. I am not a professional in the field. I don't use facts or figures or theories. I just say it as it is. I knew that my dementia was my dementia, and everyone's dementia and their own journey was unique to them, but people who worked within the caring professions or support roles or social workers needed to hear from us what we wanted when the time finally came. It was important that others remembered us as people who had lived, loved, laughed and cried, who had hobbies and passions and fears and pleasures.

Because my ability to read and write was pretty well gone, I never prepared my speeches but just stood up and talked. Sometimes I am sure I repeated things but generally – although I don't know how I did it – I kept a flow going for half an hour or so and tended to create a laugh or two along the way.

Deb used to say she didn't know how I did it either, but I had no choice: that was the only way I could do it. Once, I think it was at the Alzheimer's Society, they wrote me a prompt of things they wanted me to say, but I couldn't be doing that. I couldn't possibly follow a list of points to make. I very politely gave them their prompt sheet back and just said my own thing. And I do believe that I got a rousing round of applause and that there was standing room only in the tent where I was giving the speech.

I used to do this at the Alzheimer's Show in London too. I remember Angela Rippon interviewing me and sat and just talked to her, without notes or lines to read from. Angela was a wonderful person to chat with; she just seemed to get it. It's such a shame that I have no proper memory of this, other than the hazy, half-formed one which lingers in the corridor between my short-term and long-term memories, trying to decide whether or not it should force its way into the long-term room or disappear under the haphazard clutter of all the other memories in the short-term room. I'm glad to say that Angela is still hovering which, again, is a rather wonderful thing to be able to say!

As I have said, the only problem about making speeches like this was that because I never knew what I said; I was never able to judge if it was any good. Honestly, as soon as one sentence was complete and I started the next sentence, that first sentence would be fading. It was like my words were written in the sand and the sea washed them away all too fast. When I met Deb and she started to jot down the things I said, I felt so reassured that my words were now being written in stone. It was important for me that my words were not lost but that someone captured them. When she read them back to me, I used to think, *Gosh, did I say that! How poetical!* It was reassuring to have these words captured, but how strange it was to have a memory outside of my head! My thoughts were all too soon gone, but Deb had them for me, she held them for me, always, and I found that most strange. It was as if Deb inhabited my world more than I did sometimes.

After each talk, I would ask Deb how things went because I was genuinely interested to know what I had said barely an hour ago.

Although I enjoyed giving presentations and talking honestly about living with dementia, it did rather ram it home that I *was* living with this terminal condition. Sometimes we would come out of the hall and cycle home and I'd say to Deb that I could actually feel the dementia monster pushing me in the back, reminding me that he was there behind me. My dementia shadows felt long and dark after a light day. And these days were light; I loved engaging my brain and focusing on talking to people. But a weary mind was a slow mind and I always hoped that tomorrow would be bright and clear, and that dementia's shadows would be short and light.

When I sat down at home at the end of these days and tried to remember some of the things I had done – any of the things I had done – I realised that there was just a void there instead of a memory, I realised that the corridor ahead was just becoming that little bit narrower and I was finding it harder to squeeze through the gaps. I was just beginning to get that little bit more afraid.

DEB

(vi)

BEING AFRAID IN THE NARROW CORRIDOR

Today Peter has delivered one of his amazing talks to a group of social workers. I sit and watch them as he talks; they are rapt, caught in his wonderful web of compelling narrative. Peter does not hold back but he also speaks with humour and warmth. Even though some of what he says has become familiar to me, I love to listen to him and I love to watch others' faces as they hear him unravel the tangled ball of wool which is his dementia and show them some of the simple solutions to a complicated condition.

When he delivers his talks, Peter has said to me that he feels as if he is a performer.

"I take people from the audience by the hand, lead them into my dementia world. I show them around a little so that they get to feel what it's like to live my life, to feel and to understand my condition. I don't want to scare them; I just want them to have the opportunity for a peek around."

That's what it feels like he is doing today. He is by turn cajoling and self-effacing, witty and yet full of pathos. He talks descriptively and vividly, from the heart rather than from the mind, and I can see that, one by one, he pulls his audience behind the safety curtain of the stage and into the world that he inhabits. This is not done unkindly – far from it. Peter holds out his hand to each and every person in the audience, until they coyly accept, and then he smiles as he shows them around, he allows them a moment to be him and then, kindly, he escorts them back to the safety of their non-dementia world.

"After all, who would want to live permanently in my messy old world?" he says. "Who would want to see the dark underside of my world when I can show them the glossy cover? They don't really need to see what's inside the cover, do they? Why would I want to scare them like that! No, a little glimpse is all they need."

As we cycle back, he asks how the talk has gone and he asks, not out of insecurity or because he needs reassurance or praise, but quite simply because he has no recollection of what he has said.

My response is genuine. "Brilliant. You're such a natural public speaker. Even though it's such a serious subject, you brought it to life, and everyone was smiling and you were laughing with everyone."

Instead of his usual flippant response, Peter takes me by surprise by saying, "It's all a front, you know. If you smile at people, it's a recognisable sign and they understand what it means and will respond, but I sometimes find it hard to smile. Sometimes smiling is such an effort, such a sham." He pauses. I know he wants to tell me something that I probably do not want to hear.

"You know, I'm frightened."

And there it is. Laid out in front of me like a spatchcocked chicken, unpalatable innards displayed to make me wince and turn my head away, the drifting rancid smell enough to make me gag. I do not want to know that my friend who faces the world with a bravado shield placed firmly in front of his body and a trusty blade, which he wields at all that dementia can throw at him, is scared. I want my friend to be pedalling Pete, my cycling chum. I do not want to have our friendship bubble pricked by a rush of reality. It feels as if I am hurtling uncontrollably to something unpleasant ahead of me in the road and there is no way to avoid it. My wheels are going to get splattered in something rotten (possibly the innards of the chicken) and it will take me a good while to cleanse them.

Peter continues, "It feels like I'm living in a narrow corridor which is slowly getting smaller. I'm walking through the corridor, but every day I am finding it harder to move. And now the only way to move forward is by edging shoulder first, pushing my way through. It's like there's no room for me. I get stuck; I get jammed in the small space. And I'm frightened of what I'm going to become, of the man I will be. And then sometimes I worry that I won't remember the man I used to be."

Resolutely I keep pedalling at a steady pace, just about keeping up with Peter, moving through the countryside, the yellow rapeseed fields providing a stunningly bright backdrop to a conversation which is becoming darker by the moment.

"But, here's a thing, chum. I won't let this bloody dementia win; I won't let it control me. I've become a fighter and I'll keep fighting. I might be trapped in this dark dementia bag but I'm going to kick and punch holes in the bag to let the light in. You know, in life, most people walk towards the light, but people with this condition are walking away from it. So, here's my plan: when I have to, I'm going to walk backwards so I will still see the light."

I look up at him, Peter on his penny farthing, focusing on the road ahead, anticipating any hills or junctions so he can take appropriate action.

And then, from his lofty height, he looks down at me and says quite seriously, "You know, you have two tufts of hair sticking out through the top of your helmet. You look like the devil on a bike." And he laughs, and I have to laugh because Peter's joy at living is contagious. And whatever pity or sorrow I feel is left trailing blithely in the balmy Suffolk air as Peter, the showman, the pugilist, the friend, is back doing what he does the best: giving dementia a hearty two-fingered salute.

CHAPTER
FOUR

CHAPTER
FOUR

(i)

CAR CRASH

Peter is sitting in the back of our car as we drive home from an event hosted by Ipswich Town Football Club. Ipswich are trying to make the club dementia-friendly and, as part of the dementia awareness-raising campaign, they have asked Peter to attend a match and to feed back his thoughts about his experience. Peter has never been to a match and does not particularly like football, but it is a great attempt from Ipswich to raise awareness. Both Martin and I are football enthusiasts and so we are happy to go with him.

The match has been shockingly poor and this is one occasion when having a bad memory will be to Peter's advantage. There are probably twenty thousand other people in the ground today, for whom a quick burst of dementia might well have been a blessing!

So, here we all are in the car on our way home, Martin in the front with me, and Peter in the back. As we approach a roundabout on a main road, a car rams into the back of us. We hear that awful crunching sound of metal on metal, the physical jolt as the car stalls and then there is the vocal, emotional reaction of, "Oh my God!"

The damage to the car is substantial (in fact, the car is later written off), but Peter, from his position in the back, assures me he is fine. We drop him home and no more is said about it.

Later that evening, Teresa texts to say Peter has a stiff neck but hasn't told me as he doesn't want to upset or worry me. But it worries me and he is in my thoughts a lot for the rest of the evening.

The next day, when I send him a photo of the damaged car, his response is to ask if I have been involved in a prang. I am shocked, although I don't know why I am surprised, as intellectually I know Peter has memory issues. But I suppose to forget something as physical, visceral and frightening as a car crash really brings Peter's dementia home to me and I allow myself to sit with the feeling of sadness for a couple of days, thinking about Peter's brain and what it might be like to have lost the ability to create new memories, both good and bad.

A little later, when I post a picture of our damaged car on social media, it is clear that Peter has totally forgotten the crash. His comment of 'looks bad, hope no one was hurt' is made without a hint of sarcasm or irony. An event which, to Martin and to me, is still so raw and recent, has been wiped thoroughly from Peter's memory bank. And whilst this creates a moment of crystal-clear clarity for me that Peter has no recollection of this event, it also creates a moral dilemma. What is the best way to respond? I suppose this quandary encapsulates one of the really challenging aspects of dementia: do you patiently listen and hear the same stories over and over? Do you interrupt and say I know? Do you pretend it's the first time you're hearing this? Or, in this case, do you recount events patiently as if the listener is hearing them for the first time? Would a man such as Peter know you were doing this and would he be insulted?

I write my response on Facebook that we are all fine and then we meet later that day and I mention the crash again, to check his neck is all right.

Again, Peter has no recall of the crash, so I start to tell him the story as if it is for the first time. This whole episode gives me pause for thought. Perhaps I really don't understand the complexity of Peter's dementia; perhaps I am too blasé about his level of recall. Perhaps I am deluding myself that, because he presents as 'normal', he really does remember.

I am cross with myself for this naivety and I take some time to reassess what I know about Peter and how living with dementia is a constant challenge.

I wonder again what it must be like to have each day, each hour, each minute, each second wiped from your memory like an over-zealous schoolteacher frantically wielding an eraser? I wonder how Peter survives, being forced to live off his past memories, to return to events of several years ago for sustenance, rather than to dine out on the newly created ones which nourish and sustain those without memory loss.

Peter often says, "I remember with emotions and feelings," and, apart from the events which are embedded in his memory, there are very few new memories being created.

If I only had my memories of ten years to sustain me, I think I would wither away and, in a moment of shocking realisation, I realise that's was what it's like living Peter's life. But if I didn't even have the memories of a few minutes ago, then I really would starve. There are only the old memories for him; the doors to his memory bank are slammed shut, and nothing more is allowed in. Slowly, very slowly, I fear my friend is starving.

PETER

(ii)

DRIVING LICENCE

So, they had taken away my driving licence by now. This might not sound much, but stack this latest setback up against all the other things that dementia was stripping away from me, and perhaps you will see how devastating this was.

Imagine the freedom that you have in life: you can hop into your car, you can drive wherever you want, you can work, you go home and discuss your day with your partner. Then imagine that someone snips a little bit of that freedom fabric and it becomes smaller and tight-fitting, that you have to pull it that bit firmer to get it to cover you but you are already feeling the chill where the fabric no longer fits and your body is more exposed; that's what happened when the DVLA removed my licence. Pre-dementia, when I got home after a day's work, Teresa and I would always have a discussion about how my day was, who I talked to, who I saw, just the general ebb and flow of a conversation which most adults and couples up and down the country have. A year or two into my diagnosis, when my memory was deteriorating, Teresa would come home and ask what I'd been doing and I would pretty much be able to tell her. And then it got that I couldn't really remember how my day had been so Teresa just used to say, "Did you have a good day?" and I'd say yes, because I generally did if I'd been cycling, and that was our conversation. And now I was no longer able to drive, the last bit of my freedom had been taken from me. My world was shrinking as fast as my ability to hold a proper adult conversation. And so, my cycling had become so much more than just cycling. It was my new freedom, my only freedom and bid for autonomy. And with every turn of the pedals, I cycled away from dementia and became the man I used to be, and not the man I was fast becoming.

Cycling on my penny farthing achieved all this and more. It was such a challenge for me, both physically and mentally. The penny is a fixed wheel bike, with no gears and no brakes. It meant that I had to anticipate hills, both up and down. Once you started to go up a hill, you had to be very sure you could make it all the way up because the alternative was to fall off. Equally, when I went down a hill, I had to know what was at the bottom of that hill as I needed time to backpedal to get the bike to slow down and then enough time to jump off. I loved both aspects of this challenge.

Deb and I realised that for every one hundred calories she burned on her road bike, I burned two hundred, and so I was always hungry and devouring quantities of cake and scones; yet I was losing weight. I realised my face had become much leaner and my jeans needed the belt to be tightened a notch or two. More so, much more effort was needed to get my jeans on over the bulging calf muscles I was developing!

But I loved our training sessions and we met some wonderful people. I do remember one occasion in Woodbridge; Deb had popped into the loo and I was standing by the toilets holding her helmet out in front of me. An elderly woman approached me and asked me how much money I needed for a sandwich. I knew that lycra wasn't the most fashionable of items, but I didn't think it made me look like a down and out!

"We missed a trick there," I told Deb when she emerged from the loo. "We could have made a killing!" That sort of thing made both of us laugh, probably irrationally so, but laughter was such a wonderful thing for me to do and I think Deb picked up on this and so even irrational laughter was better than no laughter. Or tears.

Penny attracted a lot of attention when we were out, the main question was, "How did I get on and off the bike?" and so often I found myself giving little demonstrations to interested people. I didn't mind at all. I have always enjoyed talking to people and I had certainly become the centre of attention. Both Deb and I loved seeing people's faces as we cycled past them; it really seemed to me as if I was making people's day and that made me very happy.

Gradually we built the mileage up until I felt confident that I could cycle fifty miles on Penny. The next issue was: could I cycle fifty miles on Penny for six consecutive days?

We decided to cycle into Ipswich to get a sense of cycling on busier roads. We had stopped in Woodbridge when a lady with a camera rushed over to us to ask if she could take photos. This lady, Charmian, turned out to be the most wonderful support and was keen to take as many photos as we wanted. Well, the day we decided to catch the train to Lowestoft and cycle home was a great opportunity for her to demonstrate her enthusiasm! Charmian turned up at Saxmundham station at eight o'clock in the morning and travelled with us to Lowestoft, took some more photos and then we cycled back whilst Charmian went home. That type of dedication and support meant the world to me.

Meanwhile Deb and I attempted to find the route back to Saxmundham and, again, created a lot of attention and comments as we cycled through various towns.

Sometimes Deb and I would go out and we would have a route planned but it would all go horribly wrong. I was not sure if a man with dementia and a slightly eccentric woman with absolutely no sense of direction was a good combination to be let out together, but you know, we always arrived somewhere and our journey was always fun. That's what it was all about really. Just being out there, having fun, living for the moment.

"It doesn't really matter where we end up," I would tell Deb. "If we aim for Framlingham but end up in Orford, does it matter? We can still have coffee and cake. We are still moving forward. The important thing is the journey and what we make of it, not the destination."

And we both stopped and reflected on my words, and without even realising it, I had said something quite profound – or so Deb said!

DEB

(iii)

DESTINATION KNOWN, DURATION UNKNOWN

Peter says he feels a little 'cloudy' today; his dementia monster seems determined to cast a dark shadow over him and beat him down.

"But here's the thing: I won't be beaten," Peter says. He squares up to the monster, looks him unerringly in the eye, shoves a finger in his podgy chest and pushes him onto the couch at home.

And here the monster is to stay, scowling, sulking and kicking his heels. Oh, make no mistake, he'll still be there when Peter gets home – Peter knows that and the monster knows that and I'm beginning to understand that more and more – but for this moment the power dynamic has shifted and it is Peter who is in control.

"We have training to do," says Peter. "So, you know what? My dementia monster will have to learn to deal with that. I am in charge!"

So here we are again, out on the road, cycling. It is truly a remarkable sight: this extraordinary man, perched on a fifty-two-inch bike, legs akimbo as he sails down the hills, and then legs frenetically pushing as he climbs back up, his face becoming redder, his neck thrusting backwards and forwards, like a hyperactive cockerel on speed as he garners his strength to keep Penny rolling along through the glorious Suffolk countryside.

"So where are we headed for?" I ask.

"Does it matter? What's important is that we're out cycling."

His words resonate with me, and with something he had said a few days before, when he was in one of his contemplative moods.

"Dementia is a strange journey," he'd said. "Make no mistake about it, the destination is known, but the route is unclear and the duration of the journey is unknown."

He is right, of course he is, and our cycle ride today for me is a visual embodiment of that statement.

"That's why I have to do everything now whilst I can," he continues. "So, I don't mind where we go, the important thing is that we are out, cycling. If we head for Framlingham but end up in Orford – well, does it really matter? It's about the going out and the doing, it's not about where we end up."

And his words move me, as they often do. Now, it may not be immediately obvious, but I am one for taking a perfectly good metaphor and then flogging it mercilessly to death. Peter's words about his journey present me with a great cycling metaphor: I wonder how the rest of his journey will develop, what bumps he might stumble across, what random divots he will avoid, what potholes he will swerve around, how many punctures he might get. I wonder what crossroads he will reach, which direction he will turn, and at what junctions he might struggle, but equally I think about the hills he will conquer and the many miles he will triumphantly cover.

I am subdued, caught up in the tangled skein of thoughts in my head and Peter, in his intuitive way, knows my mood has dipped. He reverts to the showman, waving at people, giving a thumbs-up to all those who stop to admire Penny.

Someone leans out of his car window and says to Peter, "You made my day, mate," and I look up at Peter's face and see how he is relishing that moment. Here is a man who savours each turn of the pedals, who welcomes each part of his journey – punctures and divots included. His face is fixed in a grin of pure hedonism. He's right: the journey is the crux of it all; it is the detours and the unexpected moments along that journey that define its quality, rather than the destination itself. I feel better and smile because Peter has that knack of making people around him smile.

And so, I experience again that incredible juxtaposition of profound sadness and joyful positivity and it catches me, here, deep within my soul and momentarily – only momentarily – it sucks the very marrow from me.

Of course, the dementia monster is at home, where Peter has left it – we all know it isn't going anywhere – but Peter has triumphed for these few hours.

"All good?" I ask.

"All good. Perfect, in fact." He thinks for a moment and then delivers one more Peter Berry insight: "Do you know, we will look back on days like these, and one day these days will be the good old days."

I don't think he is aware of the tiniest of shudders which runs through me at his remark, but I know two things: those words will never leave me and Peter won't remember these days.

CHAPTER
FIVE
WINTER 2018

PETER

(i)

THE RESTAURANT THAT MAKES MISTAKES

At the same time as planning for the challenge is underway, Channel Four contacted me to ask if I would participate in their documentary, *The Restaurant That Makes Mistakes*.

It was strange how they found me. Mainly, I think, they wanted participants from the Bristol area, but they just could not find enough people willing to take part or whom they deemed suitable to take part. They found me via my Facebook page!

This was an innovative project where fourteen volunteers, all living with various forms of early onset dementia, staff and run a pop-up restaurant in Bristol, headed by chef Josh Eggleton. The project hoped to show that people living with dementia still had an active role to play in employment and, by giving people a purpose in life, their levels of self-esteem would increase.

I was more than happy to be involved in such a ground-breaking experiment. The only problem was they were filming it in Bristol and that journey was going to be very tough for Teresa and me. I couldn't go on my own and so Teresa had to negotiate time off work too. We were right: making this journey on a weekly basis was full on and it took a lot out of us. And on top of that, although Channel Four were wonderful and paid for us to stay in the same hotel each visit, thus reducing unnecessary stress for me, Bristol wasn't home and I was finding the going took a lot out of me. Things which other people would find minor inconveniences, like navigating my way down a hotel corridor to the reception or remembering where the bathroom was in our room, became major obstacles for me to overcome.

Before we were allowed to take part in the show, we were all assessed by a psychologist. She did a series of tests on each of us to see how our dementia – and we all had different forms of dementia which affected us in different ways – was impacting on our ability to function. Some of us, like me, experienced severe short-term memory loss, others had lost the ability to string more than a couple of words together, whilst others had lost their basic abilities to do the simplest of tasks, like cut up an onion. This meant that we all could work as a team and use the skills we had to help each other. It was a great idea.

The psychologist also wanted to judge the level of our self-esteem before the project and then during and after it. When I watched the episodes afterwards, I found this very moving, not just watching myself but seeing the others too. We had quickly become friends and we all looked out for each other and so to see them struggle to do elementary tasks, like remembering three words in order, really was difficult for me.

The psychologist who assessed me quickly realised how much I hid from the world about the extent of my dementia and she told me I was a showman. Well, that didn't come as a surprise! But what did surprise me was how she had me sussed! You could fool some of the people some of the time, but apparently not a psychologist!

One of the best things about being involved in this project was the fact that I was part of a team. I loved that we could all use our strengths to help each other. I knew that I couldn't remember anything longer than a few moments and that I couldn't really write things down, but I could still cut an onion with the skill and precision that only a man who'd worked in the timber industry could do. A couple of people had lost their ability to cut anything up but had the most beautiful handwriting. That was what I called teamwork! I do believe that being part of a team was a great help to increasing our self-esteem. Rather than being told we couldn't do something or that it wasn't worth telling us as we'd only forget, we were actively encouraged to problem-solve and work collaboratively.

The tables had all been clearly numbered to make it easy for us to find, but one morning when we arrived at the restaurant someone from the production team had changed the position of the tables. This was either mischief-making or a scheme to see if we were able to cope and problem-solve a little more. And, of course, we managed. Between us and because we were working so well as a team, we found a way to call upon each other's abilities and we sorted it all out. That showed Channel Four!

But I must say that Channel Four were wonderful. They had a doctor on site and a solicitor too. This was to ensure that those of us on benefits weren't filmed 'working' which might impact on our benefits. The solicitor wrote letters confirming that everything we did on this programme was voluntary and unpaid. It was thoughtful, sensible things like this which really made the show worthwhile, as none of us had to worry about the benefits office or being judged.

Whilst I don't remember much about the programme now, and much of this section was prompted by Deb and Teresa, I have watched again the scene where Josh encouraged me to type an email. As I have mentioned, writing and reading were quickly becoming skills which dementia was stripping from me, and Josh was quite insistent that I persevered with typing a fairly simple email. I could see from watching the scene how I was obviously transported back to my business days. In those days I used to routinely write fifty- or sixty-page reports in great detail. Now I could hardly put more than a few words together. So, it was odd to watch and see me on television breaking down and crying. It was a huge moment for both Teresa and for me. What it stirred within me was the importance of having a purpose in life. It reminded me again how my own self-esteem had taken such a kicking upon diagnosis; that was why I cried although I rather wished I hadn't done so on national television!

Even now, although I had absolutely no recollection of this, when Teresa or Deb reminded me of it, I still experienced the profound and raw emotion and relived it in the only way I knew how: by feelings. It was such a stark reminder that my family and I were never going to rid ourselves of this dementia monster. I could give it a face and an identity, I could tease it and curse it and given it a stern talking to, but, you know, it was always going to be there. But then, being me and being a stubborn soul, I knew that although dementia was stripping me of myself, I had become more than I ever was. I simply had to in order to survive.

So, being part of this great project was hard work but really enjoyable despite these moments of sadness. And I really hope something concrete comes from the programme, even if it is only to raise awareness of dementia and to shake up some people's perceptions of myths and stereotypes that surround the condition.

As well as meeting other people with a similar life-changing condition, it was a great opportunity for Teresa to be with the partners of those living with the condition. It wasn't exactly a holiday for her, but I believed that having an opportunity to share her concerns or frustrations – and let's face it, there were many frustrations for her, living with someone with serious memory loss – was going to be almost therapeutic for her.

I enjoyed being front of house. It was good to watch people eating together, the table full of food and drink, and to hear people laugh and chat across the table. Even though I found eating out difficult these days because of the struggle to read the menu and of being overwhelmed by too much conversation, it was good to see people just enjoying each other's company and if I helped that happen by saying, "Table for four, is it?" or, "Table for two?", then that was a good thing for me. And, do you know, I do like the ring of a sentence which says simply, "Table for four?" It makes me think of happy times, of people meeting and dining together, of community – of normal, everyday life. Yes, 'table for four' certainly has a good sound to it.

DEB

(ii)

TABLE FOR ONE

Peter is back for the weekend after filming the restaurant programme and so we are cycling again. It's a chilly day and we sit indoors at our table for our coffee break.

Peter runs his fingers across the table. I have realised that, as his memory fades, he uses his other senses to remember life's pleasures. Remembering through touch is one of these senses. There is a smile of joyous recognition on his face as he reconnects with his old, working world.

"Wood feels so familiar to me still. Wood is home. This is larch," he says. "It's a good piece of wood. It's warm to the touch; it was a living, breathing tree. It still is living and breathing. It moves and bows with the elements. That is what I feel and see now."

I have realised over the last few months that Peter instinctively knows the names of plants and shrubs, can identify the seemingly suicidal birds which all too frequently hop in our paths as we cycle, and still recognises the type of wood he sees. He might forget within moments that he has eaten a rather large slice of carrot cake and deny all knowledge of it when I remind him, but he will never forget the colour and feel of a tree. This knowledge clings to his mind, like the bark of a tree wraps itself around the trunk. Peter's love for trees is undiminished, untarnished by the relentless march of dementia.

"You know," he says, "living with dementia… well, it's a bit like living with a shrinking table. Here's a nice big table…"

Here it comes, I thought to myself. *Another bite-sized Berry maxim to remember and record.*

"Look, it's got a teapot and cake and cutlery and serviettes on it and our bike helmets and…" he stops and grins at me, "… and lots of your bits of rubbish – what on earth is that?!" (At this point, I remove my sweat-stained tissue from the table and pop it in the bin, knowing that although he is teasing me, my innate messiness offends his sense of order, order to which he still clings on to before it slips away into the cesspit of dementia obscurity.) "This table can hold so much. And so many of us, friends and family, can sit round it and share the things on it. But if you cut a bit of the table off, the cups will fall to the floor, and then the plates will fall and the cutlery until eventually there will be nothing left. And then more and more people will leave the table because there just won't be room for you all to sit around it with me. And there won't be any point in sitting around the table either. It will have nothing to offer.

"You know, my table used to hold all my memories. But then it's like someone has taken a saw to the table and cut a chunk away. The table is just not big enough to hold my memories. Some of my memories just fall off."

Involuntarily, I look at the floor as if searching for Peter's memories. I think about the table and what it contains and how painful it is for Peter to be a bystander and watch his precious memories, one by one, clinking and then shattering into the void below.

I know enough about Peter that I realise that sometimes he is able to get down on his hands and knees and scoop a handful of memories up. It is these memories which he clutches tightly to his chest and yet that he also shares so willingly with me. Memories of being bullied at school and finally, triumphantly, standing up to the bully and whacking him on the nose, and of his father congratulating him on solving the problem. Memories of his father showing him how to cut trees; memories of being wrongly accused of vandalising a phone box in Framlingham and being taken to court, where he continued to protest his innocence, and then of receiving a fine for his impertinence; memories of his first cycle trial at the age of seventeen; memories of his marriage to Teresa and the joy of that day; memories of planting a tree for his daughter when she was two. These memories are clear and tangible, and he delights in describing them to me. And yet, the memories of the recent cycle challenge, the memories of yesterday or even of an hour ago are indistinct, fuzzy around the edges now, yellowing, fading a little more with the passing of time.

Although it is painful for him to look at the pieces in his hands, those broken shards of memories, he forces himself to look, because if he lets go now, what will be left? He is a practical man; his strength has always been his ability to solve problems. I suspect he is still hoping that he can somehow repair them, piece them together, bit by bit until they are restored, then that will at least be something. On his good days, he can do this; on his cloudy days he lets them tumble, with a weary sigh of resignation, from his hands onto the floor. Some shatter into smaller fragments. If he tries too hard to retrieve them, the jagged edges will slice the tips of his fingers into painful ribbons and so he knows he must leave them on the floor where they will be trampled into the ground by the clomping footsteps of the dementia monster who increasingly, relentlessly, is stalking Peter.

It's hard to believe that just a few years ago Peter shared his table with friends and family. His table groaned under the weight of memories. His table was a place of laughter and conversation, a sociable place where he and Teresa welcomed all. Gradually, as the table has shrunk, people have moved away, muttering almost in embarrassment, making their feeble, transparent excuses as to why they can't stay.

So, I now realise that these days Peter shares the table with just a few people, but eventually we both know he will be dining alone, with the merest handful of a few random memories squashed into the small space remaining until even these are not enough to sustain him.

CHAPTER
SIX
SPRING 2019

PETER

(i)

AMERICA!

As if all of this was not enough to keep me busy, I received an email from an American, Andy Jordan. Andy had seen me do a thirty-minute interview with a colleague of his, Deborah Kan, about living with dementia and he wanted to make a documentary about me.

I found this comical but exciting. An American wanting to film someone from a tiny village in coastal Suffolk! I had to ask Deb to sort out the arrangements, as it was all too complicated for me to do, and she was happy to step in.

Again, the details of this event are a little sketchy, if I'm honest – well, to be perfectly frank, I have forgotten all about them, but Deb helped me to put the pieces together with the assistance of some photos and the actual video. But most of the account below has faded from my mind and so I am going to let Deb write this up in her own words and will have to trust her that she leaves nothing out!

DEB

When Peter told me that he was going to be filmed by an American, I was sceptical. But Andy Jordan behaved impeccably, with utmost respect and sensitivity to Peter's needs. Andy had set up a company called Needle Space Labs and, inspired by an interview he'd seen about by Peter, wanted to create a video story for his company. Andy's work 'aims to thread the needles of our time to stitch a fabric of urgent optimism and defiant joy – where stories grow business value, build movements, and elevate and celebrate the human story'. Basically, Andy's focus is very much on the positive, the human story with an upbeat feel, and Peter was an ideal fit for his ethos.

Rather than come from the US himself, he employed two London-based colleagues of his to come down to Suffolk for two days. The plan was that they would interview Peter and then film him pretty constantly, particularly when he was out on the bike.

Ollie and Pawel arrived in Suffolk and set about their task with enthusiasm; it was obvious that they found Peter both inspirational and charming. They conducted a wonderful interview with Peter: talking in front of the camera was still something he did incredibly well. I do not know how he held it together, given that he had forgotten the question by the time he finished his answer, but he invariably performed the most polished of interviews.

Although Peter was asked some difficult questions around the diagnosis and his depression, he faced them all and answered with such a disarming honesty that you would have to be made of reinforced steel not to be moved.

Ollie then interviewed me, and it was only during this process, where I stuttered and fumbled my way through his questions, that I really appreciated how incredible Peter was. Polished and practised, Peter faced the camera and the questions and retained his poise and equanimity. The best analogy I can come up with is to think of a grand piece of furniture, say a well-built and sturdy sideboard which won't rock or break under pressure, however much you pile on to it. Then think of a cheap equivalent: perhaps it's flimsy, there are bits missing, it's slightly wonky and there inevitably are pieces which just don't seem to fit anywhere or are left over after construction. As soon as anything is put on that sideboard, it will fold and collapse. That was me during my interview. So, if I call Peter a sturdy sideboard which absorbs everything which is piled on top of it, it's in the spirit of admiration.

After the interview we both were party to the surreal experience of being filmed by Pawel, who sat in the boot of Ollie's car as we cycled behind them. By the time we reached Thorpeness, it felt a little like we were being pursued by a purposeful paparazzi, although paradoxically we were behind the car, so perhaps that makes us the pursuers, not the pursued? Then, like a cinematic magician conjuring up as many different methods of media as possible, Pawel produced a drone from his bag of tricks. The drone flew over us as we cycled one stretch of Thorpeness time and time again whilst Ollie also filmed us from the side of the road.

The amount of time and effort that went into the video was wonderful. When the video was released, Andy said there was so much rich material within it, that it was seven minutes in length. There was a positive response both in the US and the UK and by the Alzheimer's Society, who said it was one of the best videos on dementia. When Peter watched it, he said it was the strangest sensation listening to the things he had said and yet still with no idea that he had said them.

"I can be pretty profound, can't I?" he said to me.

Peter was really pleased to be part of this video, but he said that the fact that he remembered so little of it was like watching his life being eroded.

"All of my memories are being created in the sand and then being washed away by the tide of dementia. I want you to write them down in stone for me so at least they will be there for Teresa or Kate, or anyone else, to access one day when my memory door is firmly shut."

I reassured Peter that everything was being recorded and that I would write it down for him.

A couple of days later he said to me, "Do you know, just the simple act of trying to remember this and being able to remember so very little has created crashing, tumbling waves in the turbulent waters of my memory. I'm trying to think of something I want to tell you, but I just can't get it into my mind."

DEB

(ii)

SOMEONE HAS THROWN A PEBBLE IN THE WATER

It is spring, it is unseasonably warm and we are able to resume our training. Peter is slightly subdued and I sense that something is bothering him and so I don't speak. There is an aura of quiet contemplation nestling between us. I have a sense that when we come to a halt, Peter might draw back the curtains on his dementia world a little more, and allow me to wander, unfettered, into his dementia house. I know there is a library of material stacked behind these curtains; a mountain of metaphors and a host of images just waiting to be accessed. Even if I can only flick through some of the cover pages, I know it will yield something stunning and make me wish for more knowledge, for further insights into Peter's world.

We have cycled thirty miles: time for a break. As I have said, I am Peter's food and drink reminder, and it's a task I do in friendship, not pity. We sit in a cafe and, uncharacteristically, order a salad and sandwich rather than cake. We do have a cycle challenge to train for, you know, it's not all about cake and ice cream!

Peter says, "I've been thinking and here's a thing: a while ago, someone had a pebble in their hands and they etched a letter 'd' on it. That 'd' was for dementia. Then they threw the pebble in the lake. It took a long time to hit the water. It stayed in the air for a long while, but it was always going to come down at some point. And when it finally hit the water, the ripple effect was huge. Because once that pebble hit the water, it created its own chaos. It didn't just ripple into my life but into the lives of those who know me and those who love me. The ripple is now a wave. I can ride on the wave, I manage, I can hang on. But the wave is going to get bigger until the water becomes choppier. You know, I've already fallen in a few times. Eventually that wave will become a tsunami. And I won't be able to surf on it or even hang on to it; my fingers will slip and I will fall off. And everything will be destroyed."

I have only known Peter since his diagnosis. His old world is closed to me. I try to imagine Peter's lake, becalmed, and then, as the pebble fell, how it gathered momentum like an Exocet missile and finally how it exploded into his world, eviscerating it, debris flying everywhere, bruising those who were unfortunate enough to be in its way.

I find Peter's image haunting. As if for support, I grasp my fork in my rather cack-handed way and prod it at my curling lettuce.

"But I am beginning to let people have a glimpse into my reality, into my world. I am letting them ride the choppy waters with me. I know it's a scary ride, but it's a ride that needs to be taken."

My grip has tightened further on the fork and my knuckles are pinched white, as if I am hanging on for dear life as I surf the waves alongside Peter. The lettuce remains pathetically, placidly on the plate. Curiously my appetite for wilted lettuce has diminished exponentially.

And then Peter says, "You know, Debs, you hold your fork like a rather demented baboon. That lettuce has got no chance of making it into your mouth," and we laugh and the trumpets bray their joyful 'tada!' as the velvet curtain tumbles down, smoothly, effortlessly, on the dementia house for another day. Move on, nothing to see here, folks, as Peter, the showman, emerges, waving at the audience, shielding his eyes and blinking slightly against the rays of the bright, shiny world he has created.

"Let's cycle," he says. He is beaming as he contemplates the next phase of the cycle ride; it is a beam which creates its own glittering shaft of light, illuminating the road ahead. But, you know, if you glance at Peter, you might see lurking behind those twinkling showman's eyes the merest flicker of sorrow as he wonders why the pebble landed in his lake. And if you listen carefully, just behind him you might hear the sound of the gathering tsunami, some way off yet, but gaining momentum.

PETER

(iii)

UNPREDICTABLE DEMENTIA

Sometimes I just didn't sleep at night; too many hours were spent looking at the ceiling, listening to my dementia monster chuckling away and chanting, "I'm still here," all pissing night.

Most people, when they go to bed, will run through the day's events in their heads. They might choose to relive the good parts and forget the bad parts. When I go to bed, I have none of that. I can't reflect on what I've done that day because I have no knowledge of it. If I have had a long cycle ride, it might be that my legs ache a little and that would be a clue to something I might have done. I won't know where I have cycled to or what I have eaten or the people I have chatted to. I might think about cycle events I had done in the past, but I have nothing to go on in the present, nothing to mull over, to relive, to enjoy.

Our bedroom curtains were always left slightly open, just the tiniest amount of the outside world accessible to me, and so on some clear nights, I could lay in bed and look at the stars. But mostly I lay in bed, in what felt like an empty hole, in the dark, waiting to fall asleep. This was a lonely, scary place to be and the nights dragged.

Sleep deprivation and dementia. That was not a good combination. It didn't seem fair. But now, there was an added complication. I wasn't only living with dementia; I was now living with unpredictable dementia. Some days I walked tall, straight and strong. Other days I was weak, bent over and old. It was like living with a wild-eyed horse: uncontrollable, unpredictable dementia.

When I lay awake all night my thoughts were just a series of emotions; it was hard to keep track of anything. But when I lay awake, with Teresa sleeping soundly besides me, I knew I wouldn't be able to get back to sleep. I felt trapped in an empty void. It felt that dementia was my nothing and when I looked ahead, in the bleak, black night, I thought I saw that nothing marching towards me, waiting to engulf me. I was stranded in no man's land, a lost soul in territory so unknown that it frightened me. I didn't know where I was or how I got there. It was a very strange sensation not to know which world you inhabited or where you belonged.

I had many thoughts, but they were gone as quickly as they arrived and I couldn't grasp any of them, couldn't pull any of them towards me. On the odd occasion when I could reach out and pull a thought close to me, it would be something totally unrelated. You know what it felt like? It felt like reading a book to page ten and then arriving at page twenty without knowing what happened on the pages in the middle. I didn't know the plot, I didn't know the characters, I was just in a strange land and I desperately hoped that someone would reach out and take me by the hand to rescue me and keep me safe before the nothing engulfed me.

When I was awake at night like this, I could feel the footsteps of my dementia monster, walking down the corridors of my mind. It took my memories and my thoughts and trampled over them but, you know, it could not take my soul or take my feelings. These were mine forever. That's what I told myself in the middle of the night. That's what I told myself in order that I could survive the blackness of the night and emerge into the morning's light.

Oh, I knew that, eventually, the night would go and morning would come and the physical world was lighter; with the new day I always had a new sense of determination. This unpredictability would not interfere in my plans. I was determined not to be trampled by this stampeding horse but to ride on its back, to tame it, to be the warrior still. It was important to me that others would not know how some days the battle just emptied me out. I did not want others to be affected by my dementia. I was still a proud man and the need to be strong propelled me along dementia's rocky path. I would not trip, I would not give in. I did not want other people to walk the path I had to walk or feel the fear I felt every day. And above all, I did not want other people to feel sad or upset by my condition. Part of my job was to protect those around me, those who I cared for and loved, from the hell of my dementia. That was a hell of a battle to fight every day.

DEB

(iv)

#CAUGHT IN THE CROSSFIRE OF DEMENTIA SHRAPNEL

My firm belief, as we plan our training rides, is that it is all going well and Peter appears to be in good spirits. Every time we are out, he jokes and laughs, and, to me, it seems he is leaving the dementia monster at home more frequently. This challenge has given him a purpose which, he says, is all he needs to maintain his spirit and his health. So, when I receive his message this morning, I am surprised. Perhaps I have got complacent about the extent of his dementia or perhaps – and this is a more likely scenario – Peter is so skilled at hiding it that it's easy to forget he is a man living with a terminal condition. The text message simply says 'cant [*sic*] put werds [*sic*] together this moring [*sic*], a bit frustrating, hed [*sic*] all mudled [*sic*]', followed by 'but #uscyclewillhelp'.

The hashtag reference deserves an explanation. Neither Peter nor I fully understand its significance or, indeed, the appropriate use of the hashtag, and yet we use it indiscriminately and without context. It amuses us: there is no reason to it other than a randomly placed, often misplaced, hashtag makes us laugh. Perhaps that's all the reason that's needed. Laughing seems to be the panacea to so many things for Peter. So even in his moment of intense frustration at his muddled brain, his use of the hashtag makes me smile.

I text back '#uscyle #somewherenice #itisthen'.

And, of course, the cycle ride does help. As well as laughter, just being outdoors is Peter's medicine, the fresh air his anti-depressant and the sights and sounds of the countryside (and forgive me for this blatant plagiarism, Shakespeare) act as a balm to his hurt mind. His spirits lift and the cloying thick cloud which was clogging his thoughts earlier seem to dissipate a little.

We cycle, we chuckle, we chat. Our idle chatter is of the most inconsequential kind and we sprinkle it in joyous handfuls over the roads as we cycle, where it floats like stardust, glitters briefly, disintegrates and then is no more. This is the beauty of these bike rides. The cycling is the reason to be, the conversation is secondary unless it is to marvel at some piece of nature which Peter delights in pointing out to this naïve townie who still doesn't know the difference between a Caprifoliaceae and a myosotis and, sadly, probably never will.

So, there is an unexpected moment of pathos when, sandwiched between the airy badinage of our trivia, Peter says, "You know, this dementia sucks. I wouldn't wish this condition on my worst enemy. But even more than that, I don't know what's worse. Having the condition or knowing I've got the condition or maybe knowing what's coming towards me at some point. What do you think?"

Although Peter willingly offers me his shoes to stand in so I can attempt to understand what it is like for him, his shoes will never fit me. For those living with dementia, there is no 'one size fits all'. There is no way I can ever fully understand and certainly no way I can answer a question like this.

He continues, "Dementia isn't like other terminal illnesses; there is no treatment. With cancer, the chemotherapy might buy you some quality time when you feel better and you can plan stuff. But this isn't the case with dementia. I know what's coming. I don't know how quickly it's coming. But I know it's coming. It's gathering momentum in the distance… it's coming."

He pauses, grappling around in his mind for one of his amazing descriptions.

"I feel like the dementia monster is looking at me through a mirror, but it's my reflection I see in the mirror, and then he's leaning over, grabbing me by my neck and dragging me towards him. I don't want to go to him. I will fight him every day, every single day. It's a tiring battle, but it's a battle I'm going to fight. I am the warrior fighting dementia. It's like a war, you know, a real battle, this dementia business."

There is another lull in the conversation.

"But," he says, "here's a thing. Dementia is like riding a penny farthing: hard to master at first but very possible to do with perseverance." And there it is, another Peter Berry classic, almost throwaway remark. But it feels as if this particular observation encapsulates the very essence of Peter.

"Never mind," he says, "it's a beautiful day and we're out cycling. What could be better? Mind that dead grouse; it'll make a hell of a mess on your tyres." And he has slammed the door shut with a soft but firm thud, blocking out the dark elements of our conversation and allowing a prism of light to shine back onto our day. #Peter #showman #returns.

When I get home, there is a strange pain in my side; is it possible that a tiny shard of dementia shrapnel, the merest sliver, the fallout from the latest skirmish, has somehow lodged itself under my skin? Is it possible that I have become part of the battle, albeit in the smallest way, and am starting to feel Peter's angst? Even if this pain flickers within me for only the briefest of moments, it still provides me sufficient light with which to illuminate the dark corridors of Peter's world. It's a glimpse and an understanding that I am privileged to be given. #trying #to #stand #inPeter's #shoes #fighting #the #battle

DEB

(v)

Peter's father, Jimmy, died just before the cycle challenge. He had been in a home for a while, but his Alzheimer's had progressed to the point when quite often, when Peter visited, he could not remember who Peter was. I knew that Peter struggled with the whole concept of visiting his father, as it was like looking at his reflection and seeing into his own future, and this was something that he found incredibly emotionally stressful to do. I also knew that his relationship with and love for his father meant that he wanted to visit him. It was a tough dilemma for him.

When I first met Peter, he would visit his father pretty well every week, taking the opportunity to cycle to the home in Framlingham and thus combining the activity he loved with a job he often dreaded.

To Peter's immense credit, he never told either his mother or his father that he had been diagnosed with dementia.

"They both went to their graves without knowing," he told me. "It just wouldn't have been right for them to know."

And, again, I marvel at the inner strength of a man who would protect his parents at any cost.

Peter would tell me how Jimmy would ask at every visit, "Where's Mother?" and the pain of explaining that Betty had died a few years ago was too intense. Rather than make Jimmy relive his grief at his bereavement, the family decided to tell Jim that she had gone on a bus journey.

"She likes a bus journey, does Betty," Jimmy would say.

"She does," Peter would agree.

"Where's she gone?" Jimmy would ask.

"To Lowestoft," Peter would say.

"Oh, she likes that. She'll have a good time there. That's good."

And then no more would be said.

Peter said to me that Jimmy often said, "Who are you?" and he'd say, "It's Peter, Father," and Jimmy would say, "No, Peter's only a little boy of five."

At first Peter would take the time to explain that he was Peter and all grown up. But realising how much confusion, and then distress, this caused to his father, he decided to tell Jimmy that he was just passing through visiting someone else – he'd gesticulate to a man in a chair nearby – and say that he thought it would be friendly to greet Jimmy; Jimmy used to like that and they'd chat away happily.

"Dementia is a complicated condition, surrounded by simplicity," Peter said to me. And in this case the simplicity was to minimise the pain to Jimmy. So, it was absolutely fine to avoid telling Jimmy the truth and I understood that. As Peter said, the lie did not hurt anyone and it protected Jimmy. It was a simple solution to the complexity which dementia presented every day.

But this in itself was not much a dilemma for me until, just before the cycle challenge in June 2019, when Peter and I were cycling past the home where Jimmy used to live, Peter said, "My father lives here. We should go and see him."

It was obvious that Peter had forgotten the recent death of his father. I hesitated and simply asked Peter if I could tell him the truth.

He was insistent that I did and when I told him that Jimmy had died, he laughed and said, "Well, I must have looked a bit of a knob then. Fancy forgetting he'd died. Father would have found that funny, he would have laughed!"

Humour aside, Peter's message was crystal clear: he demanded the truth. Peter's wish was spoken from his position of knowing; when the time came when he no longer knew, I wondered if he would want the same pain-free responses that he had given to his own father.

I was silent for a while and then slightly shaken when Peter added, "Sometimes I look into your eyes and I know I've told you the same story before, but you pretend you haven't heard it anyway. Am I right?"

And, although he was right, I did not know how to respond to this. There was no easy answer: "Yes, you've told me," was unnecessarily harsh and an unwanted reminder of Peter's memory loss. Saying, "No," was a lie and I did not want to compound one lie with yet another lie. Rightly or wrongly, I chose to lie when I thought it was the simple option. If Peter told me one of his stories twice or three times, did it matter? The lie softened the dementia blow. From Peter's perspective, surrounding dementia with simple solutions was to alleviate unnecessary pain and angst and so, I had decided, this was what I would do, and, you know, every time I heard one of his stories, I heard something a little different, something which added to my own understanding of his life. Quite simply, too, I just enjoyed hearing the pleasure in his voice when he was telling me something which made him smile. But, in hearing the same story more than once, I also learned something about people's stories: whatever people have to say, and however many times they say it, there are generally layers upon layers of meanings and subtext within their sentences. More importantly, with people living with dementia, their stories contain the essence of who they were before dementia crept up on them, so actually, it's always worth listening just that little bit harder.

CHAPTER
SEVEN
SUMMER 2019

PETER

(i)

THE MAIN EVENT:
THE FOUR COUNTIES CHALLENGE, SUNDAY MORNING

This was what I remembered about the challenge. We left at around the end of June and we cycled for a few days. I completed the event entirely on my penny farthing. I am pretty sure that I had a wonderful time. Why wouldn't I have had a wonderful time? I was cycling. That's what I do: I cycle and I pedal down dementia. You see, cycling had become my salvation; my very heartbeat had become a turn of the pedals in my mind. You can only pedal forwards, not backwards; that was the important bit. I pedalled forwards for those days and I realised that the world was a wonderful place when viewed through my cyclist's eyes. Where there were dark and sinister shadows forming from the spectre of my dementia, there was now light and joy.

That was what I remembered about the challenge.

DEB

(ii)

This is what I remember about the challenge. Oh, where to start! There was so much information to process, we met so many people, there were just so many things that needed to be said, and that were jostling around in my head, vying for my attention.

The first thing to say would be that we completed an amazing cycle challenge. Without the still-stricken Jan, there were four of us (Peter, Mark, Mike and me) who cycled the entire distance, every mile of the journey, every turn of the pedals. But only one of us who did it on a penny farthing!

It was sad but true that, apart from Peter, we would all have a story to tell in the future. Despite Mark having been in a serious motorbike accident some years before which had left his leg stiff and painful, he said to me that he was looking forward to telling his grandchildren that he had been a part of this challenge. Mike, too, was delighted to be involved and chuffed that, even with his bad knees (he had gone through surgery a short while back), he was physically able to participate. I was staggered that, despite my still-creaky shoulder (and my sticky-outy bone), I was about to embark on this ride. It was not without a certain quirky irony that three of us were physically damaged in some way and the fittest participant was Peter. Fit, as he always said, but only, alas, from the eyebrows down.

All of us were excited and yet one of us would forget all too quickly. We all knew that once Peter's muscle-weary legs were better and were no longer a physical reminder of his achievement, the event would be erased from his memory. For the rest of us, it was an event which would stay with us forever.

Indeed, when Peter and I discussed this challenge a couple of months later to get his perspective on it for this book, it became obvious that most of it had simply evaporated from his memory. He wasn't angry about this, though. If anything, he was just a little melancholy about the fact that an amazing six days had disappeared into the distant haze of his other short-term memories.

"I remember with feeling," he said. And he pounded his heart for emphasis. "What I need you to do is to write about it in as much detail as possible. You know, my thoughts are being set in stone from sand," he observed. "Dementia has taken my sand, but not my stone." And he grinned at me and said, "You are now my stone."

I looked suitably aghast at being entrusted with such a task.

"You hold the key to unlocking my memory, but even then, the key probably won't work for more than a few minutes before it rusts and the door is locked once again. So, all you have to do is to write about it. No pressure, then!"

Peter was trusting me to remember, to understand and to preserve whatever I encountered when I unlocked his life with the key. The key which Peter handed over to me was both a burden and a gift. It was a privilege and yet the responsibility frightened me a little.

I reminded Peter that I had kept a blog, a light-hearted look at the adventures we experienced during our training. The blog and many pictures of our training appeared on his Facebook page and had elicited a positive response from his readers. I talked Peter through this to see if any of my musings or people's comments would jog his memory, but they didn't.

However, what this talk did produce was another classic Peter thought. We were sitting down, flicking through the blogs, looking at pictures, trawling through anything which might creak open his memory door a fraction to let me in, when he said, "Here's a thing: the moment has become the moment, just the moment. I am the now; the now is me."

When he saw my frown, he looked at me, almost pityingly as it was obvious, I didn't immediately understand.

"What I mean, Deb," he said, "is that I forget all previous conversations and events from moments ago. All I know is this moment as we live it and speak it. So, I'm afraid there is no chance of me remembering the cycle challenge, even though it was only a couple or three months ago. That particular door has slammed well and truly shut."

Given this, I have written the account of our amazing challenge using my own memories which are still crystal clear. I knew that Peter's canvas was virtually blank, with just the vaguest outline in pencil sketched across the canvas, and even that was in danger of being rubbed away by dementia's determined airbrush. But my canvas was vibrant, a busy, bustling place, alive and well, containing stories to be shared. It was like a Bruegel picture, with so much going on, with activities at every glance at the canvas. It felt so unfair that I was able to hoard my memories and lift them out whenever I wanted to relive those moments, whereas Peter had virtually nothing left of the challenge.

What was apparent to me, and only by virtue of being allowed a peek into Peter's dementia world, was that throughout the whole challenge Peter remained resolute to keep the showman side of himself on view. He took it as a personal challenge – as if cycling on a penny farthing was not challenge enough – to hide the true extent of his dementia from as many people as possible, even including some of the entourage. So, as well as the momentous achievement of cycling fifty miles a day on Penny, Peter made a live video recording at the end of each day for his Facebook page and then joined us all for an evening meal (and a pint) and often would not return to the hotel until ten o'clock in the evening. This might not sound particularly arduous, but, with the dementia monster perched on his shoulder and pushing him further and further into the ground, you must believe that it was. If you looked carefully into Peter's eyes you could sometimes see a weariness etched deep inside, but he was damned if he was going to show it if he could avoid it.

Of course, Teresa saw it – it never left her – and she saw it much more vividly and intensely than I did. I am not so naïve to think that I always saw the true picture; Peter would always paint the canvas as cheerfully as he could, full of light and vivid colours, just so I didn't see the bleak, grey part of his life. Teresa saw it; Teresa lived with it and was aware of every change in Peter's memory. Peter said that those around him were more acutely aware of his 'failings' than he was and so this was another reason why they 'suffered' with dementia and he lived with it.

Teresa once said to me it was her job to protect Peter. Teresa knew it and lived it with Peter, and the challenge took its toll on her. Teresa, as Peter recently said to me, was joined to his dementia, whereas I was just connected, and these were subtle differences. The rope connecting me allowed me to move away from it and put it out of my mind. Teresa was bound permanently to the dementia rope and would never be free. As Teresa put it, she was all too frequently 'dementia'd out'.

Despite her obvious pride at Peter's achievement, her worry and fear sat heavy with her. But Teresa, like Peter, had learned the techniques of a true showman and she rarely showed her worry or agitation in public. Here was yet another terrible example of how dementia was a diagnosis for the whole family and the whole family experienced it together in some shape. Peter's dementia was Teresa's dementia and between them they moved it deftly from place to place, from hotel to hotel, efficient and expert hauliers of a private, heavy burden.

For those six days, Peter described himself as a 'regular normal bloke'. Although this 'regular normal bloke' was cycling ridiculous distances at a considerable pace on a penny farthing and this 'regular normal bloke' was also running on empty for most of the evening. And yet Peter found the inner strength to push his dementia to one side without collapsing in a heap. As he observed later, "Dementia leans heavy on our shoulders and that makes it difficult to stand tall."

I believed that throughout the entire challenge, Peter was standing as tall as any human and for that he deserves our admiration.

On the day of the challenge, 23rd June – see, that date was etched in my mind and I did not have to look it up to verify it – I could sense there was an aura of high excitement. I swiftly cycled the three miles from Saxmundham and arrived, heart pumping and endorphins flowing, at the village green in Friston to see Peter with the broadest, widest beam on his face. If evidence was ever needed of his skill of living in and relishing each moment, then it was there for all to see. This was his moment to feel joyous, to sense anticipation – his moment to be. He was clasping it in his hands, holding it as if it were a quivering, fragile bird, not wanting to let it go. There was almost a sense of (an understandable) greed – Peter wanted all of this and more; Peter was quite simply loving the anticipation of what was to happen and yet he knew all too well that it would disappear and would never be seen again.

There was a crowd around Peter and I could see that he was talking to a reporter from ITV Anglia news. His ability to talk to the camera had become second nature. He was fluent and articulate and, although the substance of the questions might have curled up in his memory even as they were spoken, like the yellowing pages of an ancient book, Peter did not let on. When we saw the news item on ITV a couple of days later, we were all so incredibly proud of him but certainly not surprised by another virtuoso performance.

To add to the sense of occasion, the villagers of Friston had pulled out all the stops to wave us off. There were refreshments and people waving balloons, just chatting happily about the amazing event which was about to unfurl. People just wanted to be there to support him.

One of Peter's Facebook followers, a Scottish lady called Ann, had made the journey from Bury St Edmunds (about an hour's drive away) with Alistair, her husband, to wave us off. Even better, Ann had made some shortbread, and for me, with the lingering burden of the misanthropic old days still slung, like Dick Whittington's worldly goods, over my shoulders, I was deeply touched by this gesture. She did not have to do this; she chose to do it. It helped that the shortbread was authentically Scottish and simply delicious.

So, there I was, in the early morning watery summer's sun, in a field in a tiny village in coastal Suffolk, munching on homemade shortbread. Martin had already arrived and was taking pictures, looking proud of us all, although not quite managing to shed the look of a man who quite simply thought his wife was batty even to consider undertaking this venture. I could hear people's conversations and laughter; I could smell the coffee wafting over from the church hall. I was aware of the general levels of excitement mounting. I stood there, slightly self-consciously, and I took a moment to reflect on what I was doing a year ago and how my perspective on life had changed.

One year ago, I had been wading knee-deep through the mire of other people's lives. I worked with families living in poverty; I worked with young women – some as young as thirteen – who allowed themselves to get pregnant by equally young men whom they knew would never stay around long enough to see the baby's first smile or hear its first giggle or see the tiniest glimpse of a white tooth peeking through its gums. And, the longer I worked within this sector, the more I had felt an overwhelming sadness growing within me as I knew what damaged and bruised fruits the next generation would yield.

I had watched teenagers carry knives in an all too cavalier manner as if they were the latest must-have fashion accessory. I saw too much and, as I watched from the outside, my fingers spread over the grimy window of their lives, peering in, feeling helpless to stop them from doing so, I knew I could do nothing to change things. After years of working and trying, I could see no discernible change.

I read articles in the newspapers about the term 'early intervention', where the notion was bandied about as if it were the magic solution to society's problems. Old ideas had been repackaged, rebranded and sold to us as the cure-all to youth crime and poverty. Who were these government ministers and youth workers who felt they had the solutions? Who were they that they thought they had the answers to such an endemic? Did they think we were fools?

Recently, Peter had used the phrase 'educated fools' and now, reflecting back, I think I realised I had been surrounded by educated fools. And the biggest fool had been myself for staying in a job which sapped my energy and left me empty.

My balance had been skewed and one of the reasons we had moved to Suffolk was to find a better equilibrium and to rebalance me before I fell and was left, like a spinning bottle, revolving slowly around on the floor, not knowing where to stop or if I ever would stop spinning.

Looking back, I hadn't realised how lost I was and how stale I had become. With apologies to Shakespeare, like Macbeth, I had been in the excrement of human lives stepped in so far returning were as tedious as go o'er. But at that moment, as I stood in a field in Friston I was finally able to go o'er. I had something that Macbeth never had: I had Peter.

And so, as I stood by my bike, about to cycle three hundred miles with one of the kindest, funniest, wisest people I had ever met, with a man who was living with a condition so crushing that most people would have buckled, I took this moment to reflect, to let go of the past and to allow myself a smile, knowing that Peter had played a major role in refocusing my blurred and damaged vision. This was my seminal moment: this was my Suffolk moment.

Peter had brought me to this place of calm where people were positive and genuinely wanted to be part of something and where they had been touched by one man's story and just wanted to be there. The contrast could not have been starker. For that moment, on that day, more than any other day over the last year, I felt I had arrived and the dirty, finger-stained smears over my vision of life had been wiped clean. I grabbed Peter's arm probably more vigorously than was necessary. "Thanks," I said.

Understandably, he looked puzzled by my effusiveness but, being Peter, smiled and said, "I'm glad you're here. I wouldn't be doing this challenge without you."

Like a pilgrim, I had arrived in Suffolk to find a new path, and if I had been religious, I would have said that this moment was my epiphany. I had no religious faith but what I was blessed with was a restoration of my faith in humanity even if it came packaged in the shape of a man dressed in lycra, living with a debilitating, terminal illness, about to climb onto a fifty-two-inch penny farthing and cycle three hundred miles into unknown territory.

(iii)

DAYS 1-6

Several people from the Sax Velo cycle group set off with us. We must have looked an interesting crew: eight people on road bikes behind one man on a penny farthing, like baby chicks following a parent, with unerring faith that they were going somewhere safe. Which, as Peter later said, was a bit weird, really, putting our trust in a man living with dementia who couldn't remember where we were heading from moment to moment.

We cycled to Woodbridge for our first coffee break. The reporter from ITV met us there and interviewed Peter again. There was a real buzz around us and the overwhelming sense that we were part of something special and wonderful. How privileged we were to be here, with Peter, joining him on his journey, on his battle against dementia, being part of his army trying to shoot dementia down, albeit too briefly.

Our first lunchtime stop was Ipswich and then, after that, we were venturing into unknown territory. Each day brought new and wonderful things, but the biggest common factor was that people were genuinely delighted to see us. Over the course of the week we drew in over £800 in cash donations from strangers.

I was overwhelmed by people's responses during the challenge: the support and goodwill was evident as we cycled through East Anglia.

I had posted on Peter's Facebook page details of our itinerary, including our lunchtime stops, just in case anyone wanted to join us on our cycle ride. One further incredible endorsement of the effect Peter was having on other people was that during two of these lunchtime stops, two couples independently had travelled up to meet him, just to say 'hello'. Both couples had a partner who was living with dementia and it was amazing to watch Peter chat to people whom he did not know if he knew or not, to make them laugh, to put them at their ease. I had never known a charismatic personality quite like Peter.

This put into perspective for us all the effect that Peter was having on others living with the condition. They greeted him as if he was their friend, although, in reality, they had only known him virtually. The impact Peter had – and will continue to have – on others' lives was clearly huge.

On our third day, Peter conducted a live interview with BBC Radio Suffolk. Only Peter could have carried off this interview with such insouciance whilst dressed in cycling gear, sipping coffee, in a crowded cafe.

The penny farthing was most surely having the desired effect of attracting attention. As we stopped for coffee in Abingdon, an elderly lady started to chat with us. She then took the trouble to contact Young Dementia UK and made a very generous donation, and she wrote an article in the local parish magazine appealing for further donations.

Equally as we hit the homeward trail, we stumbled across a group of people having a reunion from their school days some fifty years ago. Peter gave an impromptu lecture on his penny farthing and his condition, and we collected £80 from them. It was gestures like this which, for me, continued to restore my faith in human beings. There were good people out there; it appeared I just needed a gentle reminder.

As we crossed the finishing line there was a look of utter triumph, joy and love on Peter's face, and it was an image which I hoped would never leave me. That was the supreme moment for Peter: he had challenged himself to an arduous act of physical endurance and not once had his dementia monster managed to deter him. Whatever doubts he had experienced, he suppressed; whenever fatigue threatened, he stood tall and brave, Canute-like, and held back the force of the dementia waves. Peter was king for those six days and, even if he was going to be exhausted that evening, it did not matter to him. Peter had taken his dementia monster, laid him flat and put one victorious leg onto the monster's stomach.

As we dismounted, Peter turned to me and said, "The roll of the wheels is the dynamo that generates my day."

CHAPTER
EIGHT
JULY 2019

PETER

(i)

PADDLING MY OWN CANOE

The challenge was over. I still felt a sense of triumph, but I also felt empty and knew that I needed another target, and quickly!

It was just over a year since I had met Deb. We sat down and talked about writing this book; we discussed her first year in Suffolk and how, since that time, my life had changed a little more, how more of my abilities had deteriorated. We talked about all the things that I had done, some with her support, some without. I had to flick through Facebook and some of the pictures to conjure up some sort of memory, but I felt we had done a lot. Most of my memories were now done with feeling rather than with my mind.

This much I did know. It had been an astonishing year. And yet, despite having achieved so much, I felt as if I needed a fresh challenge. I loved the cycling, and nothing would replace that, but I also knew that I needed something else in the future to motivate me.

I mentioned to Deb some thoughts about a new challenge, but nothing really felt right. Any long challenge would involve

SLOW PUNCTURE

overnight stops, and this would involve Teresa having to take time off work. With all her goodwill, it was not really something she felt she wanted to do, either emotionally or financially. I fully understood that. Teresa was my rock and I needed her by my side to cling to. I needed my rock, but she, with her other responsibilities, did not need her stone around her neck, which is what I was going to be.

The other thing was, it was hard to predict how I would be this time next year. And that was a scary thought so it was better to put it out of my mind, which, to be honest, was not that hard for someone with memory issues to do.

To fill the time whilst I was thinking things over, I might have suggested to Deb that I fancied something water-based. I might have suggested that I liked a challenge! I might even have hinted that she would be more than welcome to find us something exciting and fresh to do. These South London girls – they were rather efficient sometimes because, before I realised it, she had had organised a canoeing activity for me and Teresa, Martin, and her and two friends of hers (Fliss and Stewart), whom I had met previously but obviously not remembered.

I do know that Teresa was full of doubts about going canoeing because she feared the unknown and she was uneasy about falling into the water. But, do you know what? She loved it. Deb has shown me a picture she took on her mobile phone. When I look at that photo, I am moved by our expressions. Both Teresa and I were calm, like the water, and we were both grinning at the joy of being in the fresh air.

If ever there was a picture where a hidden disability was extremely well hidden, this was it. We looked like a normal couple, out for the day with friends. We didn't look like a couple living with dementia.

You know, sometimes I sit at home, when the dementia

curtain closes a little and I need to rest, and I think about my life.

It can be hard to collect my thoughts; my dementia canoe sails very gently down the Alzheimer's stream and I don't want to get too close to the edge of that stream. The drop is sheer and there is no way back. I make myself paddle upstream, sometimes even singing to myself to ward off the sound of the lapping waves below. The day we took the canoes out was special, even though the memory has long since gone. I know that I was paddling upstream, well away from the edge; I know that I couldn't hear any noise other than my own inner peace and sense of calm. I know that I loved it.

I texted to Deb later that day: "I got to paddle my own canoe… dementia left my side and was nowhere in sight… I forgot my condition, I forgot dementia. How wonderful is that."

And then I got to thinking, as I sat in that canoe, in the middle of the Norfolk broads. I was surrounded by water and nature and could occasionally hear Deb and Martin involved in a heated discussion about which way she should pull her oar, and then Deb invariably pulling it in the wrong direction! I was half laughing at the way their canoe was spinning around in circles but also half thinking about where I was, and I became focused on the just being there, on the physical effort of rowing and guiding the canoe and then, after a while, my mind started to flicker and then it lit up and all sorts of thoughts tumbled in to my head. Most of the thoughts have gone, but I remember one.

We were cycling again the next day after the canoeing. I pointed out to Deb that, for me, living with dementia was like paddling a sinking canoe. I was not able to recall what I said after that, or to explain more fully, but I certainly had the image very much in my head and I couldn't really shake the image off for the rest of that day.

DEB

(ii)

LIKE A COLOSSUS ASTRIDE HIS CANOE

As ever, we are cycling. I say to Peter, "We went canoeing yesterday. I really enjoyed it." I have learned not to say, "Do you remember?", as I know this annoys him, although he doesn't show it. Who would want to be asked, "Do you remember?" when the chances are that they do not?

So, I have learned this new skill, this way of starting a sentence which does not acknowledge that Peter probably has forgotten but will, at the same time, remind him of something we have done.

I still never really know if Peter does remember the things we have done or if he chooses to say he does so he minimises how much I might be upset by his memory loss. I certainly don't know if he remembers the canoeing outing with any clarity or whether there is just the vaguest thread hanging on there in his head, but whatever he does recall has triggered another one of his prophetic insights.

"Here's a thing," he says, "living with dementia is like paddling a canoe. I'm paddling away and getting to where I want to be and then a hole appears in the canoe. That's not a problem at all because I can find something to plug the hole with. The problem gets bigger when another hole appears. It's very random when it happens. I can fix or conquer one hole, but it's hard to keep fixing them all. Maybe I'm sinking?"

My eyes remain on the road ahead as I cycle, but my mind and my heart are transported to the lake where only yesterday Peter was enjoying a dementia-free day. But now, instead of the calm lake where we all had such fun, I can see Peter paddling frantically through his dementia-infested waters. This water does not have crocodiles lurking beneath its murky depths. It has something much worse: these waters are clogged with fears of the future, congested with regrets and choked with a sadness which can neither be fully defined nor completely repaired.

Peter keeps this emotional turmoil under the surface and, like a colossus, stands astride his canoe, beating the fears down with the oars. He will not let them invade the canoe – he must not; he will not! But they are stubborn, these fears. They won't be silenced; they want their say, and so they tap their nasty little heads on the base of the canoe with a steely determination – tap, tap, tap – until they are finally able to wriggle, tadpole-like, through a hole in the canoe, that tiny hole in the corner, which Peter has not seen or managed to repair. And there they sit, Peter and his fears, suckled by his dementia, and weaned on the jelly from his brain cells. A battle royal commences: sometimes Peter turfs them overboard, back into the water where they spin, whirl and sink to the bottom, but sometimes he cannot toss them out, he just hasn't the energy, and they sit beside him, in the canoe and stare up at him, unblinkingly. Waiting.

I think Peter realises that my imagination has rocketed off in a maudlin direction. And so, apropos of nothing in particular, he says, "You know, my grandmother never saw a doctor in her life. She never registered with one."

I am relieved to be rescued from the relentless suction of the dementia waters and to be pulled back onto *terra firma.*

"What about the dentist?"

"No, not the dentist either."

"What if she had a toothache?"

Peter says, as if it was the most obvious solution, "Ah, well, then she'd go see Uncle Hubert, you see."

Reassured by the fact that his late grandmother's teeth had been in good hands, as it were, I ask, "Oh. Was he a dentist?"

To which Peter replies, "No. An undertaker."

Ah, that wonderful juxtaposition of a serious reflection about his dementia onto a family anecdote just sums Peter up. The glass-half-full approach continues to be defiantly displayed, but I know that the haunting, disturbing image of the canoe and of the sinister shapes bobbing just beneath the water will never really leave me now. I know that I am also waiting for the next hole to appear and for Peter to be left, in bewilderment, trying to plug the hole. And I know, with a depressing certainty, that the day will come when that hole will simply refuse to be plugged.

AUTUMN 2019

The weather has changed and we are probably only going to do one or two more long cycle rides before the rain and chill sets in. We both feel sad, as if we are going to lose an old shared friend. We have just cycled to Framlingham; we are sitting at our favourite cafe and having a discussion about friendship and what it means to both of us.

"It's very strange," says Peter. "I have known you for over a year now and yet I don't know you. I don't really know anything about you. I'm sure you've told me, but I have no idea what you were like as a teenager, what it was like growing up, if your parents are alive, what your relationships have been like, what you did for a job; it's like you're a stranger. And yet, and yet... I feel very connected to you emotionally."

I sit and think this through. He's right. It's a very one-sided relationship in this respect. I know so much about Peter, about his father and his family, about his emotional state, his fears and his hopes and, of course, about his dementia. I too have shared with Peter some of my thoughts and emotions; it's inevitable that, when two people spend so much of their time together cycling and writing, little pieces of their lives are going to be unwrapped, coyly, shyly perhaps, but unwrapped, nonetheless. During the time I have known Peter, I have become a grandmother, and that is a pretty major life event. Peter loves to see photos of the baby and has his own regrets that he will probably never get to share in the joy of being a grandparent; and yet, there are large moments in Peter's day when he quite simply does not remember I am a grandmother.

Friendship can be exposing and yet this exposure is just one way. So, whilst I know many of Peter's stories and adventures and can probably now complete many of these anecdotes for him, such is the capacity of my memory, each time Peter and I meet, it's as if I am a shadowy stranger, full of potential intrigue and mystery. And yet I am also so very familiar to him. I can't imagine what that must be like and the thought makes me slightly uncomfortable, as it has only now dawned on me that this is the case.

"What do you know about me?" I ask.

He pauses. "You have... two sons, I think?"

"Yes."

"I know Martin, of course, and I know he likes a bit of cake. Although I don't know what he looks like until I see him."

There is a longer silence.

"Erm, I know you like cycling!" He is trying to blag it now.

I know that he knows me so well, and yet he does not know me at all.

"I just have to use some instinct or my heart to know if I can trust people," he says, "because I can't base my feelings on facts anymore. And that makes some of us with dementia quite vulnerable emotionally, don't you think?"

But before I can answer or grow sad, Peter seems to know it's time to change the subject. Even though he professes not to know me, he knows that he does not want to cause me unnecessary hurt or distress. Peter is, I have come to realise, extremely emotionally intuitive and sensitive to nuances. Perhaps that is something that has come with his dementia, a sort of protective cover for himself as well as for others. Often, he has said that he did not want to be a burden to me by making me go cycling when perhaps there might be something else I would want to do. The thought of being a burden is an anathema to him, as well as a reality which creeps on apace daily.

"They look nice," he says. He has seen the custard tarts.

"Have one, then!" I prompt. "Go on!"

"Ooh, that's a good idea. I do like a custard tart," he confesses.

We have some fun, discussing the merits of the custard tarts for a few moments, the pros and the cons, the calorific intake versus how many calories have been expended during the cycle ride. And then, as his mind recalibrates onto something else, I realise he has moved on.

He says, "So, I've been thinking about our next challenge."

"And?"

"And... well here's a thing. Yesterday is lost and forgotten; tomorrow shall be mine for a short while. I'm always looking forward to tomorrow. My yesterdays will now always be my tomorrows. There is a new dawn rising to cast a shadow over my dementia. I don't yet know what the challenge will be, but I do know that there will be one."

I look at him, open-mouthed.

"Will you write that down?" he asks. "That was quite good, wasn't it? Well, I think it was. I don't really remember it now."

"It was more than good. Here's a thing," I say. "...it was stunning."

And Peter grins at me and brushes at his shoulders, as if he is contemptuously pushing his dementia monster off, just to show that he is still boss, albeit briefly, and I know that he has already forgotten his eloquence.

"So, are you going to have that custard tart?" I prompt.

He looks genuinely delighted at the prospect. "Ooh, that's a good idea. I do like a custard tart," Peter says, and a darting chill rushes at me headfirst, burrows itself through my skin and curls itself deep within my core, where it remains, gnawing away at me: in those few moments since the thought came into his head, he has already forgotten it. Sometimes, he is such a superb showman, with a wonderful ability to look at his dementia and to call its bluff, that I am surprised when I have a sharp, painful nudge in the ribs, like this one, of the continuing failures of his short-term memory. And I am acutely aware, too, that the gaps in his short-term memory are becoming more frequent. And in that moment, too, I perhaps get a sense of what it is like to live the same moment again and again, and yet, somehow, in Peter's world, it is a different moment. It is disorientating and I feel a little lost. This is Peter's life: living and reliving the same scenarios, and yet not knowing.

However, like Peter, I will not be deterred; for as long as possible, I will be there with him to focus on the can-dos and this next can-do will be his challenge.

I know that whatever challenge he has in mind, even if – like the much-vaunted custard tart – he will forget it almost as quickly as it takes shape, will involve some type of bike: a penny farthing, a road bike, a mountain bike – perhaps a tandem (although, with my own safety paramount, I really hope not!). I know with utter certainty that I want to be part of that challenge.

"Anyway, the challenge." There is a glint of merriment in his eyes. I realise he has something planned and was teasing me all along. "So, here's a thing," he says. And he pulls a leaflet from the pocket of his cycling shirt, a conjurer waving his next magic trick in my face. The leaflet is from Alzheimer's Research UK and it challenges people to cycle to raise money for research.

"We can cycle our local routes and there are no overnight stops."

It's a challenge designed almost specifically for Peter's needs, it would seem. The hardest part of the challenge is that the cycling must be done over the cold and miserable winter months. This challenge is perfect: it will motivate and inspire and refocus Peter's mind onto what he does the best.

"There is a choice of distances: three hundred miles, five hundred miles or a thousand... we could do the five hundred miles," suggests Peter, but he knows and I know that this will not be enough.

"Or the thousand miles," I say, and his face lights up.

"I knew you'd say that!" he beams. "Or maybe, just maybe, we could do the thousand miles and then a little more. Well! What do you think?"

I have developed a habit of rubbing my still-painful shoulder and I realise my default position seems to be to do this when I need to think or prevaricate. I rub it again, as if I am finding an excuse not to cycle more than a thousand miles, and then I remember that I am sitting opposite a man with a terminal condition.

The nagging pain in my shoulder is no more than an irritating speck of dust in the atmosphere when compared to the dark clouds which one day will burst and disgorge their destructive bile over Peter's world.

"Because," he continues, "my story is not over yet. And my message is that all of us with dementia have more to add to their stories and we will all carry on for as long as we can."

His utter belief and focus on living in the moment have never been more obvious. For me, Peter has refocused my life; he has reached out, beyond his dementia monster, and gently touched my soul, leaving an indelible mark on me. I must be involved in his epic and courageous journey as he cycles down towards dementia. I want to be by his side when he leaves his dementia monster behind yet again, when he abandons it for another day, another day in which Peter can claim a victory. Who wouldn't want to be a witness to that? But most of all, I want to be part of Peter's journey because I know that, with every turn of those pedals, he will find his salvation.

Notes

The Four Counties Cycle Challenge raised over £12,000 for Young Dementia UK, which, coupled with the funds raised during Peter's first challenge, took the total raised for the charity to £19,500.

The recent Cycling Down Dementia challenge, on behalf of Alzheimer's Research UK (November 1st 2019 to January 31st 2020), raised over £1,500. During this time, Peter cycled 1,600 miles, much of this in the rain and wind of a typical Suffolk winter on his 1950s Claud Butler!